Football

(Soccer)

New Developments in Physical Training Research

Jan Hoff and Jan Helgerud (Eds.)

Norwegian University of Science and Technology. Department of Physiology and Biomedical Engineering.

The authors:

Jan Hoff, 52 years, PhD in Exercise physiology, MSc in Sport Sciences. Associated Professor at Norwegian University of Science and Technology, Faculty of Medicine, Department of Physiology and Biomedical Engineering. Research area is biological responses in strength and endurance training for top sports as well as patients. 40 articles in international research journals with referee. Funder and rector of College of Sports at University of Trondheim. Player – football (soccer), European handball and athletics/sprint. Head coach for Norwegian national team in athletics-sprint. Coach and President for Alpine Skiing in Norwegian Ski-Federation. Manager Strindheim SC in Norwegian Premier League. Consultant and adviser for several Premier League/Champions League football teams and players in Scandinavia and UK.
Contact info: email: Jan.Hoff@medisin.ntnu.no phone: +47 92609936, fax: +47 73598613

Jan Helgerud, 46 years, PhD in Exercise physiology, MSc in Sport Sciences. Associated Professor at Norwegian University of Science and Technology, Faculty of Medicine, Department of Physiology and Biomedical Engineering. Research areas are limitations of oxygen consumption and physiological responses to endurance and strength training for top sports as well as patients. 43 articles in international research journals with referee. Faculty positions at Norwegian University of Sport and Physical Education and at Department of Sport Sciences at Norwegian University of Science and Technology. Cross-country skier, orienteering runner and soccer player. Head coach for Norwegian national team in cross-country skiing. Advisor for the Norwegian Olympic Training Centre. Consultant for several Premier League/Champions League football teams and players.
Contact info: email: Jan.Helgerud@medisin.ntnu.no phone: +47 91821892, fax: +47 73598613.

Contents

Introduction

Papers:

Strength and endurance of elite soccer players.
Wisløff U, Helgerud J, Hoff J.

Maximal squat strength is strongly correlated to sprint performance in elite soccer players.
Wisløff U, Castagna C, Helgerud J, Hoff J.

Aerobic endurance training improves soccer performance.
Helgerud J, Engen LC, Wisløff U, Hoff J.

Maximal strength training enhances running economy and aerobic endurance performance.
Hoff J, Helgerud J.

Pre-season concurrent strength and endurance development in elite soccer players.
Helgerud J, Kemi OJ, Hoff J.

Soccer specific aerobic endurance training.
Hoff J, Wisløff U, Engen LC, Kemi OJ, Helgerud J.

Soccer specific testing of maximal oxygen uptake.
Kemi OJ, Hoff J, Helgerud J, Engen LC, Wisløff U.

Endurance training into the next millenium; Muscular strength training effects on aerobic endurance performance: A review.
Hoff J, Helgerud J, Wisløff U.

Gender differences in strength and endurance of elite soccer players.
Helgerud J, Wisløff U, Hoff J.

Non-dominant leg training improves the bilateral motor performance of soccer players.
Haaland E, Hoff J.

Introduction

Football (soccer) is one of the most widely played sports in the world, where players need technical, tactical and physical skills to succeed. In part professional soccer is a question of selection rather than development. The approach used in this book is entirely connected to development of players' skill, primarily their physical resources.

Individual technique, tactics and physical resources share importance when evaluating performance differences in soccer. The average importance of each of these first level analytic approaches to differences in performance is close to 1/3 (Fig. 1).

Figure 1: **Analysing differences in soccer performance**

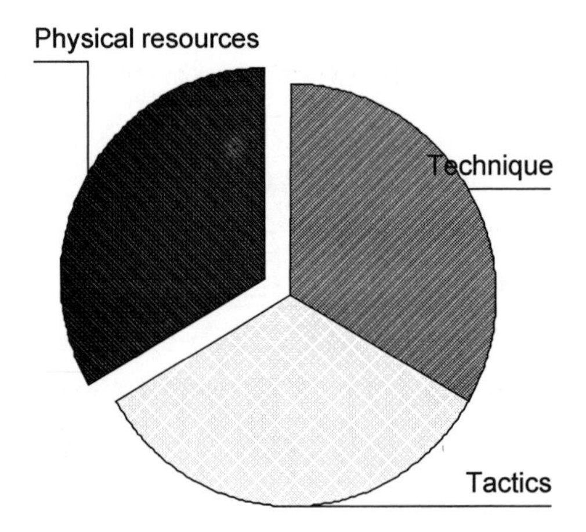

Within physical resources strength and power share importance with endurance, and each of these elements contribute to explain differences in soccer performance.

Endurance training – new developments

Previous studies demonstrate a significant relationship between maximal oxygen uptake (VO_{2max}) and both distance covered during a game and number of sprints attempted by a player. During the match a soccer player covers 8 to 12 km distance at an average intensity close to lactate threshold (LT), or 80-90% of maximal heart frequency. The high intensity bouts which is dependent on anaerobic or alactatic energy sources are only restored using aerobic energy. This makes it necessary for the player to spend substantial time at an intensity lower than LT. Mean of VO_{2max} of elite soccer players is normally reported between 55 and 65 $mL \cdot kg^{-1} \cdot min^{-1}$ with few individual values higher than 70 $mL \cdot kg^{-1} \cdot min^{-1}$.

The training background leading to these values are normally variations in soccer play, running, or interval running like "doggies" or other variations of aerobic/ anaerobic work bouts. Analyses of which elements in oxygen transport that limits the aerobic endurance have recently revealed differences between trained and untrained subjects. Whereas untrained subjects are limited by the muscles ability to utilise available oxygen, trained individuals are primarily limited by the hearts ability to pump blood (Wagner 2000, Richardson 2000). The stroke volume of the heart has been claimed to be the most important factor when considering that it can be twice as high in the trained athlete compared to sedentary people. Recent studies have further shown the importance of a large stroke volume. In textbooks stroke volume and heart frequency is described as increasing linearly during increased work rates until about 40% of VO_{2max} where stroke volume reach a plateau or only increase modest in both trained and sedentary persons. Gledhill et al. (1994) and Zhou et al. (2001) have addressed the levelling off in stroke volume. They found that stroke volume increased continuously with increased workload up to VO_{2max} in well trained subjects. In sedentary subjects and modest trained subjects the classical levelling off was found. The increased stroke volume up to the level of VO_{2max} in trained athletes has been the background for using high intensity training intervention in our endurance training. A soccer player is able to maintain repetitive bouts of this intensity level for 3 to 8 minutes. As this intensity far exceeds lactate threshold increased lactate levels are observed and has to be reduced between each work period.

This is the rationale behind using app. 3 minutes break between the intervals at an intensity level of 60-70% of maximal heart rate, which has been shown to reduce blood lactate at the highest rate (Hermansen and Stensvold 1972).

Strength training – new developments

In most textbooks the muscles ability to produce force is described as a function of the muscles cross sectional area. Recent research have shown that neural adaptations might play a major role in developing force (Sale 1992), but there seems to exist a consensus that the neural adaptation is limited to a starting period of 6-8 weeks of strength training. Behm and Sale (1993b), however, indicated that it might be the intended rather than actual movement velocity that determined velocity-specific training response. Voigt and Clausen (1990) did show that maximal strength training (high force-low velocity) with emphasis on intended rather than actual movement velocity might enhance maximal velocity (low force-high velocity) in the same movement. Hoff & Almåsbakk (1995) and Almåsbakk and Hoff (1996) have shown that high loads emphasising maximal mobilisation of force in the concentric action is extremely effective producing high velocity – low force movements. This type of training has been shown to have great effect on sprint and jump performance important for soccer play, without changes in body weight, supporting the neural adaptation theory (Hoff et al. 2001, Hoff et al. 2002). The training intervention used in the experiments in this book are thus half squats, few repetitions (4-5), 4 series and maximal emphasis on mobilisation of force in the concentric action.

Few experiments are made to investigate strength training effects on endurance performance.The training regimen described above was effective based on neural adaptation rather than muscle hypertrophy. Thus, the most valid argument from endurance research that strength training increases body weight and thereby might impair endurance performance, might not be a valid one. The endurance and the strength interested researchers at our department joined forces in hypothesising that maximal strength training based on few repetitions and high loads with emphasis on maximal mobilization of force would improve an aerobic endurance performance. First, the maximal strength training resulted in improved work economy i.e. reduced oxygen cost at a standardised aerobic workload in double poling for cross-country skiers (Hoff et al. 1998, Hoff et al. 2002). Later, we have showed that also running economy improved from maximal strength squat training with 4.7% in two experiments in this book. The maximal strength training using high loads, few repetitions, 4 series and emphasis on fast mobilisation of force in the concentric action have shown great training responses on sprints and jumping height as well as aerobic endurance, due to improved running economy.

References

Almaasbakk, B. & Hoff,J., Coordination, the determinant of velocity specificity, *J Appl Physiol*, 80(5): 2046-2052, 1996.

Behm D.G. and Sale D.G. Intended rather than actual movement velocity determines velocity-specific training response. *J Appl Physiol* 74(1):359-368, 1993.

Gledhill N, Cox D, Jamnik R. Endurance athletes' stroke volume does not plateau: major advantage in diastolic function. *Med Sci Sports Exerc.* 26: 1116-1121, 1994.

Hermansen L, Stensvold I. Production and removal of lactate during exercise in man. *Acta Physiol Scand.* 86(2):191-201, 1972.

Hoff J, Almåsbakk B. (1995) The effects of maximum strength training on throwing velocity and muscle strength in female team-handball players. *J. Strength Cond. Res.* 9(4):255-258, 1995.

Hoff J, Helgerud J. and Wisløff U. (1999) Maximal strength training improves work economy in trained female cross-country skiers. *Med. Sci. Sports Exerc.* 1999:31(6):870-877.

Hoff, J., G.O.Berdahl, S. Bråten. Jumping height development and body weight considerations in ski jumping. In: Science and Skiing II, Müller, E., H. Schwameder, C. Raschner, S. Lidinger, E. Kornexl (eds), Verlag Dr. Kovac, Hamburg, 403-412, 2001.

Hoff, J., J. Helgerud, U.Wisløff. Endurance training into the next millenium; Muscular strength training effects on aerobic endurance performance. *Am J Med Sports*, 4:58-67, 2002.

Richardson RS. What governs skeletal muscle VO_{2max}? New evidence. *Med Sci Sports Exerc.* 32:1:100-107, 2000.

Sale D.G. Neural adaptation to strength training. In: Komi (ed) The Encyclopedia of Sports Medicine III: Strength and Power in Sport. Oxford, Blackwell Scientific Publications. 249-265, 1992.

Voigt M. and Klausen K. Changes in muscle strength and speed of an unloaded movement after various training programmes. *Eur J Appl Physiol* 60:370-376, 1990.

Wagner PD. New Ideas on Limitations to VO_{2max}. *Exercise Sport Sci Reviews*, 1:10-14, 2000.

Zhou B, Conlee RK, Jensen R, Fellingham GW, George JD, Fisher GA. Stroke volume does not plateau during graded exrcise in elite male distance runners. *Med Sci Sports Exerc.* 33: 11: 1849-1854, 2001.

Strength and endurance of elite soccer players

ULRIK WISLØFF, JAN HELGERUD, and JAN HOFF

Department of Physiology and Biomedical Engineering, Faculty of Medicine, and Department of Sport Sciences, Norwegian University of Science and Technology, N-7005 Trondheim, NORWAY

ABSTRACT

WISLØFF, U., J. HELGERUD, and J. HOFF. Strength and endurance of elite soccer players. *Med. Sci. Sports Exerc.*, Vol. 30, No. 3, pp. 462–467, 1998. **Purpose:** The major purpose of the present study was to examine whether there exists a relationship between preseasonal physiological tests and performance results in the soccer league. Further, it investigated maximal oxygen uptake and maximal strength in proportion to body mass for soccer players. A secondary aim was to establish some normative data of Norwegian elite soccer players. **Methods:** Two teams from the Norwegian elite soccer league participated in the study. **Results/Conclusion:** The present study supports previous investigations indicating a positive relationship between maximal aerobic capacity, physical strength, and performance results in the elite soccer league. It is concluded that for soccer players, maximal oxygen uptake should be expressed in relation to body mass raised to the power of 0.75 and maximal strength in relation to body mass raised to the power of 0.67, when the aim is to evaluate maximal aerobic capacity when running and strength capacity among players with different body mass. Midfield players had significantly higher maximal oxygen uptake compared with defense players using the traditional expression, $mL \cdot kg^{-1} \cdot min^{-1}$, while no significant differences were found expressing maximal oxygen uptake either absolutely ($L \cdot min^{-1}$) or in relation to body mass raised to the power of 0.75 ($mL \cdot kg^{-0.75} \cdot min^{-1}$) among players grouped by position. There was a significant correlation ($r = 0.61$, $P < 0.01$) between squat 1RM and vertical jump height. Vertical jump heights for defense and forward players were significantly higher compared with midfield players. Mean results from the laboratory test were 63.7 $mL \cdot kg^{-1} \cdot min^{-1}$ or 188.6 $mL \cdot kg^{-0.75} \cdot min^{-1}$ for maximal oxygen uptake, 150 kg or 8.0 $kg \cdot m_b^{-0.67}$ for 90° squats, 79.9 kg or 4.4 $kg \cdot m_b^{-0.67}$ for bench press. Mean values of vertical jump height were 54.9 cm. **Key Words:** SOCCER PLAYERS, STRENGTH, VERTICAL JUMP HEIGHT, ENDURANCE, AEROBIC CAPACITY

Efforts to improve soccer performance often focus on technique and tactics at the expense of fitness and applied physiology. During a 90-min game, elite level players run about 10 km (4,6,37) at an average intensity close to the anaerobic threshold (7,32,40). Within this endurance context, numerous explosive bursts of activity are required, including jumping, kicking, tackling, turning, sprinting, changing pace, and sustaining forceful contractions to maintain balance and control of the ball against defensive pressure.

Previous studies demonstrate a significant relationship between maximal oxygen uptake ($\dot{V}O_{2max}$) and both distance covered during a game (7,37) and number of sprints attempted by a player (37). Rank-order correlation between average $\dot{V}O_{2max}$ and placing for the first four teams in the Hungarian First Division Championship was shown by Apor (2). Mean $\dot{V}O_{2max}$ of elite soccer players is normally reported between 55 and 65 $mL \cdot kg^{-1} \cdot min^{-1}$ (14,27,33,39,42,45–47), with few individual values over 70 $mL \cdot kg^{-1} \cdot min^{-1}$. There is some evidence that differences in physiological demands exist among offensive, midfield, and defensive players, based on a presumption of higher endurance demands on the more active midfield position. Several studies have concluded that midfield players have higher $\dot{V}O_{2max}$ values when expressed per kilogram body weight (14,30).

Comparisons of $\dot{V}O_{2max}$ using the traditional expression $mL \cdot kg^{-1} \cdot min^{-1}$ are both very routine and functionally imprecise. The oxygen cost of running at a standard velocity does not increase in direct proportion to body mass. Similarly, $\dot{V}O_{2max}$ does not increase in direct proportion to body mass (10,23). Dimensional scaling of geometrically similar individuals suggests that the cross-section area of the aorta will increase in proportion to the square of height (L^2) while body mass is dependent on body volume, which varies according to L^3 (3). Consequently, $\dot{V}O_{2max}$, which is primarily limited by maximal cardiac output, should be proportional to body mass (m_b) raised to the power of 0.67 ($m_b^{0.67}$). This dimensional scaling approach was supported by Bergh et al. (10) who found that $\dot{V}O_{2max}$ relative to body mass raised to the power of 0.75 was most indicative of performance capacity in running. Since defense players might be consistently heavier compared with midfield and forward players, as found by Davis et al. (14), they will be underestimated using the traditional expression $mL \cdot kg^{-1} \cdot min^{-1}$.

0195-9131/98/3003-0462$3.00/0
MEDICINE & SCIENCE IN SPORTS & EXERCISE®

Submitted for publication October 1996.
Accepted for publication October 1997.

TABLE 1. Physical and physiological characteristics of players.

	Age (yr)	Height (cm)	Mass (kg)	[Hb] (g·dL^{-1})	Hct (%)	VC (Liters)	FEV$_1$ (Liters)	FEV$_1$/VC (%)	$\dot{V}O_{2max}$ L·min^{-1}	$\dot{V}O_{2max}$ mL·kg^{-1}·min^{-1}	$\dot{V}O_{2max}$ mL·kg$^{-0.75}$·min^{-1}	f_{cmax} (beats·min^{-1})
Total (N = 29)	23.8 (3.8)	180.9 (4.9)	76.9 (7.0)	15.1 (1.1)	45.1 (2.9)	5.3 (0.7)	4.8 (0.6)	90.5 (5.0)	4.9 (0.5)	63.7 (5.0)	188.6 (14.0)	192 (7.6)

Strength and power share importance with endurance in soccer. Maximal strength refers to the highest force that can be performed by the neuromuscular system during one maximum voluntary contraction (1RM), whereas power is the product of strength and speed and refers to the ability of the neuromuscular system to produce the greatest possible impulse in a given time period. Maximal strength is one basic quality that influences power performance; an increase in maximal strength is usually connected with an improvement in relative strength and therefore with improvement of power abilities. A significant relationship has been observed between 1RM and acceleration and movement velocity (11,24). This maximal strength/power performance relationship is supported by jump test results as well as in 30-m sprint results (36). By increasing the available force of muscular contraction in appropriate muscles or muscle groups, acceleration and speed in skills critical to soccer such as turning, sprinting, and changing pace may improve (7). High levels of maximal strength in upper and lower limbs may prevent injuries in soccer by increasing the cross-section area of muscles and strength and mobility of tendon and ligaments (31,32).

Different tests have been used for evaluation of strength parameters for elite soccer players. Most studies (14,15,25,33) have used isokinetic equipment with different speeds and joint angles, making direct comparisons difficult. Muscular power has traditionally been measured by means of vertical jumps, and reported values are between 50 and 60 cm for elite soccer players (19,20). Raven et al. (28) used one repetition maximum bench press to test muscle strength of professional soccer players and reported a mean value of 73 kg (SD = 4.0).

Dimensional scaling must also be considered when evaluating strength measures (3). In two geometrically similar and quantitatively identical individuals, one may expect all linear dimensions (L) to be proportional. The length of the arms, the legs, and the individual muscles will have a ratio L:1, the cross-section area L^2:1, and the volume ratio L^3:1. Since muscular strength is directly proportional to the muscle cross-section area, and body mass (m_b) varies directly with body volume, whole body muscular strength measures will vary in proportion to $m_b^{0.67}$.

In the present study, cardiovascular endurance capacity as well as muscular strength and power were evaluated in two teams of Norwegian elite soccer players. Data were collected to test the following hypotheses. First, a difference exists between the two teams regarding maximal strength and aerobic endurance. Second, a relationship exists between results from the physiological tests and placing in the elite soccer league. Third, $\dot{V}O_{2max}$ and maximal strength do not increase in proportion to body mass. Fourth, no position-specific differences for $\dot{V}O_{2max}$ exist for players due to mass differences. Finally, a secondary aim was to establish normative data of Norwegian elite soccer players.

MATERIALS AND METHODS

Two teams from the Norwegian elite division participated in the study. One of the teams in the study, Rosenborg, is the most successful team in the elite soccer league in Norway in the last 8 yr and is also presently successful in the Champions League. The other team, Strindheim, was elevated to the elite league for the first year at the time of the study. Physiological assessments were made of 29 players (13 defense players, 7 midfield players, and 9 forward players) in their preparatory training phase (March). Eight of the players tested were members of either the Norwegian national team (non-age restricted) or Olympic team (under 23). Each subject reviewed and signed consent forms approved by the Human Research Review Committee before participating in the study. Physical and physiological characteristics of the subjects are presented in Table 1. All of the players within a given team were assessed on the same day, and the tests were performed in the same order. Upon entering the laboratory, hemoglobin (Hb), hematocrit (Hct), and lung function were measured for normative data comparisons. For Hb and Hct determination, blood was drawn from a fingertip and analyzed immediately using the Refletron (Boehringer Manheim, Germany) and Ames microspin (Bayer Diagnostic, Germany) devices, respectively. Vital capacity (VC) and forced expiratory volume in one second (FEV$_1$) were determined using a flow screen (Jaeger, Germany). After these preliminary tests, subjects completed a 20-min warm up at approximately 50–60% of $\dot{V}O_{2max}$. Vertical jump height was determined using a force platform (Scan Sense AS, Norway) in combination with software developed specifically for the platform. Jump height was determined as center of mass displacement calculated from force development and measured body mass. Strength testing consisted of one repetition maximum of bench press and of squats (90° angle of the knee joints) performed with a competition standard Olympic style bar and weights (T-100G, Eleiko, Sweden). The athletes were familiar with both movements as part of their regular strength training programs.

After the strength tests, each athlete ran for 10 min on a motorized treadmill (Challenger LE5000) at 50–60% of $\dot{V}O_{2max}$ before measuring $\dot{V}O_{2max}$ and maximal heart rate (f_{cmax}). The specific procedure for $\dot{V}O_{2max}$ and f_{cmax} determination is routinely used and has been previously described (22). The speed of the treadmill was increased every minute to a level that brought the subject close to exhaustion

TABLE 2. Results from the laboratory tests.

Position	Height (cm)	Mass (kg)	$\dot{V}O_{2max}$			Squats			Vertical Jump (cm)	Bench		
			$L \cdot min^{-1}$	$mL \cdot kg^{-1} \cdot min^{-1}$	$mL \cdot kg^{-0.75} \cdot min^{-1}$	(kg)	$(kg \cdot m_b^{-1})$	$(kg \cdot m_b^{-0.67})$		(kg)	$(kg \cdot m_b^{-1})$	$(kg \cdot m_b^{-0.67})$
Defense ($N = 13$)	182.2 (4.5)	81.3 (6.3)[a]	5.0 (0.5)	61.5 (3.3)	184.6 (14.9)	153.6 (27.7)	1.9 (0.4)	8.1 (1.3)	55.1 (6.5)[a]	83.5 (18.1)	1.0 (0.3)	4.8 (1.0)
Midfield ($N = 7$)	179.6 (4.2)	72.3 (7.4)	4.8 (0.5)	66.4 (5.7)[b]	193.5 (13.7)	130.8 (18.6)	1.8 (0.2)	7.1 (0.6)	50.5 (4.4)	74.6 (16.5)	1.0 (0.2)	4.3 (0.8)
Attack ($N = 9$)	179.3 (5.3)	75.6 (6.5)	4.8 (0.4)	63.5 (3.5)	187.2 (13.3)	147.5 (23.8)	2.0 (0.3)	8.0 (0.9)	57.6 (5.1)[a]	79.8 (10.7)	1.1 (0.2)	4.5 (0.5)

[a] Significantly higher than midfield players ($P < 0.05$).
[b] Significantly higher than defense players.

after approximately 5 min. Inclination was constant at 3°. Immediately after $\dot{V}O_{2max}$ determination, each subject ran for 2 min at an exercise intensity of 50–60% of $\dot{V}O_{2max}$ directly followed by a supramaximal intensity run, resulting in exhaustion after ~3 min. Heart rate (f_c) was determined using short range radio telemetry (Polar Sporttester, Polar Electro, Finland). The highest heart rate frequency during the last minute of the supraintensity run was recorded as f_{cmax}. Oxygen uptake ($\dot{V}O_2$), minute ventilation ($\dot{V}_E$), and breathing frequency (f_b) were measured during work using an Ergo Oxyscreen (Jaeger EOS sprint, Germany). Allometric equations was used to determine the relationship between maximal oxygen uptake/maximal strength and body mass; $\dot{V}O_2 = a \cdot m_b^b$ and $1RM = a \cdot m_b^b$, where a is the mass coefficient, m_b is the body mass in kilograms, and b is the reduced exponent, the numerical value of which can be obtained from the log-log plot of the experimental data, as the logarithmic expression is a straight line ($\log \dot{V}O_2$ or $\log 1RM = \log a + b \cdot \log m_b^b$) (3).

Statistical analyses. The results are reported as means ($\bar{X}$) and standard deviation (SD) calculated by conventional procedures. One-way ANOVA was used to determine differences of parameters between different playing positions. A P value ≤ 0.05 was considered statistically significant.

RESULTS

Rosenborg became champions while Strindheim ended last in the Norwegian elite soccer league. Rosenborg also did win the Norwegian elite soccer cup and participated in the Champions league. Rosenborg players had higher values of $\dot{V}O_{2max}$ and squat 1RM as a team compared with players from Strindheim (Table 3). There was a significant correlation ($r = 0.61$, $P < 0.01$) between squat 1RM and vertical jump height. There were no significant differences in squat or bench press 1RM between the three different playing positions. Vertical jump height, however, was significantly higher in defense and forward players compared with midfield players. Defense players were significantly heavier than midfield and forward players.

Neither $\dot{V}O_{2max}$ nor maximal strength does increase proportionally to body mass in elite soccer players. The exponent b was found to be significantly less than unity for the entire group, and the mean value was 0.66 (SD = 0.04), 0.55 (SD = 0.06), and 0.74 (SD = 0.06) for $\dot{V}O_{2max}$, bench press, and squats, respectively. Thus, both the oxygen uptake and maximal strength per kilogram of body mass were inversely proportional to body mass. Midfield players had significantly higher $\dot{V}O_{2max}$ compared with defense players using the expression $mL \cdot kg^{-1} \cdot min^{-1}$, whereas no significant differences were found expressing $\dot{V}O_{2max}$ either absolutely ($L \cdot min^{-1}$) or in relation to body mass ($mL \cdot kg^{-0.75} \cdot min^{-1}$) among players grouped by position (Table 2). Average results of squats were 150 kg (SD = 17.2) or 8.0 $kg \cdot m_b^{-0.67}$ (SD = 0.9), for bench press 79.9 kg (SD = 13.6) or 4.4 $kg \cdot m_b^{-0.67}$ (SD = 0.8), and for vertical jump height 54.9 cm (SD = 5.3).

DISCUSSION

In the 1995 season, Rosenborg became champions in the Norwegian elite soccer league, while Strindheim ended last. In addition, Rosenborg won the Norwegian elite soccer cup and participated in the Champions league. Rosenborg also participated in the Champions league in the 1996 season and had qualified for the quarter-final round. The results of the present study support previous investigations indicating a positive relationship between endurance capacity, physical strength, and performance results in elite soccer. As only two teams participated in the study, more work has to be done before conclusions can be made, but it seems natural regarding all the advantages the more endurance- and strength-trained individuals will have compared with less well-trained counterparts. Higher level of endurance capacity and 1RM squats compared with Strindheim (Table 3) will give Rosenborg a better base for on-field performance regarding playing intensity and power abilities such as acceleration and movement velocity among others (12,24) as discussed below.

Mean $\dot{V}O_{2max}$ in the present study (188.6 $mL \cdot kg^{-0.75} \cdot min^{-1}$ or 63.7 $mL \cdot kg^{-1} \cdot min^{-1}$) was in the upper range of values normally reported, and to the authors' knowledge, mean $\dot{V}O_{2max}$ for Rosenborg (Table 3) is the highest ever reported for a professional soccer team. This, hopefully, reflects that the volume and/or the methods of training in soccer have been improved. Compared with other sports, $\dot{V}O_{2max}$ reported in the present study is not very high. It is the authors' view that professional soccer trainers should try to elevate the aerobic power of their team players. Considering $\dot{V}O_{2max}$, it would be reasonable to expect about 70 $mL \cdot kg^{-1} \cdot min^{-1}$ for a 75-kg male, or about 205 $mL \cdot kg^{-0.75} \cdot min^{-1}$ independent of body weight. In activities

TABLE 3. Comparison of results between the two teams.

Team	Height (cm)	Mass (kg)	$\dot{V}O_{2max}$ L·min^{-1}	$\dot{V}O_{2max}$ mL·kg^{-1}·min^{-1}	$\dot{V}O_{2max}$ mL·kg$^{-0.75}$·min^{-1}	Squats (kg)	Squats (kg·m$_b^{-1}$)	Squats (kg·m$_b^{-0.67}$)	Vertical Jump (cm)	Bench (kg)	Bench (kg·m$_b^{-1}$)	Bench (kg·m$_b^{-0.67}$)
Rosenborg (N = 14)	181.1 (4.8)	76.9 (6.3)	5.2 (0.4)[a]	67.6 (4.0)[a]	200.2 (8.4)[a]	164.6 (21.8)[b]	2.1 (0.3)[b]	9.0 (1.2)[b]	56.7 (6.6)	82.7 (12.8)	1.1 (0.3)	4.6 (0.7)
Strindheim (N = 15)	180.8 (4.9)	76.8 (7.4)	4.6 (0.5)	59.9 (4.1)	177.1 (13.5)	135.0 (16.2)	1.7 (0.2)	7.3 (0.8)	53.1 (4.0)	77.1 (16.5)	1.0 (0.2)	4.3 (0.8)

[a] Significantly higher than Strindheim ($P < 0.05$).
[b] Significantly higher than Strindheim ($P < 0.01$).

that involve dynamic work with large muscle mass, as in soccer, it is generally assumed that $\dot{V}O_{2max}$ primarily is limited by maximal cardiac output (3,16). This should be taken into consideration when choosing training regimen for endurance training. Interval training, with a working intensity above 90% of maximal heart rate, primarily increases the maximal cardiac output. Rosenborg has, in previous seasons, organized the endurance training purely as playing sessions and reached satisfactory results this way. Whether endurance training should be organized as a playing session or as pure running must be considered by each team. Monitoring the training intensity during a playing session, with the assistance of a heart rate monitor, will be helpful in this regard. Experience tell us that there are problems in getting high enough intensity during a playing session, especially for teams in the lower divisions.

Several studies (7,30) have reported the average intensity of a soccer game to be around anaerobic threshold (80–90% of f_{cmax}). In two consecutive 45-min continuous work bouts, it will be physiologically impossible to work at an average intensity markedly higher than the anaerobic threshold. Expressing the intensity as an average value hides important factors incorporated during a game and provides less information. Soccer has periods with high intensities that result in accumulation of blood lactate and must necessarily lead to periods with low intensity for elimination of lactate. Most time spent in a soccer game is doing aerobic exercise, but during the most decisive and interesting situations, intense anaerobic exercise is performed.

Players should ideally be able to maintain the same level of effort throughout a game. The commonly found decline in distance covered, ratios of high intensities to low intensity work, f_c, blood glucose levels, and blood lactate levels all indicate a reduction in activity levels as a game progresses (17,18). Players with a high $\dot{V}O_{2max}$ have a faster recovery and greater stores of muscle glycogen (3,5,18). A correlation between $\dot{V}O_{2max}$ and number of sprints attempted by a player as found by Smaros (37) is not surprising in this context. As the stores of muscle glycogen are reduced, an increasing part of substrate utilization must be taken from metabolism of fat. Athletes with better endurance capacity would be expected to "spare" glycogen during moderate intensity exercise, providing greater reserves for fueling intense sprints in the later, often decisive stages of a game (29). This glycogen sparing effect would be a distinct advantage because players could run longer and at a higher intensity before reduced glycogen contents, and accumulation of blood lactate forces them to reduce their work rates and the quality of technical and tactical elements (17,18).

High blood lactate level and decreased muscle glycogen are usually connected with impaired neuromuscular performances (3). The negative impact of high levels of blood lactate on coordinative function was demonstrated in a study by Ekblom (18); players were able to juggle the ball on average 64 times consecutively before a hard training bout, compared with 3 times immediately after the training bout (blood lactate level approximately 15 mmol·L^{-1}). These factors suggest that players with the highest values of $\dot{V}O_{2max}$ and overall endurance capacity will have the potential to participate in more decisive and interesting situations. In addition, they will be able to perform technical and tactical elements at a higher intensity. Full glycogen stores in the muscles may last for about 90 min (13), and glycogen sparing may have little effect. If this is the case, focus should be attended to maximizing the stores of muscle glycogen before games and training. Saltin (35) and Ekblom (18) found that players with low glycogen content in their thigh muscles at the start of the game covered 25% less distance than others. An even more marked difference was noted for running speed; players with initially low glycogen content covered 50% of the total distance walking and 15% at top speed compared with 27% walking and 24% sprinting for the players with initially high muscle glycogen levels (35).

$\dot{V}O_{2max}$ was proportional to $m_b^{0.66}$; i.e., the oxygen uptake per kilogram of body mass displayed an inverse relationship to body mass. This is in agreement with previous studies (10,23) and supports the argument that dimensional scaling should be used when comparing individuals with different body mass. Thus, it is reasonable to expect light individuals to have a higher oxygen uptake per kilogram of body mass than their heavier counterparts. $\dot{V}O_{2max}$ proportional to $m_b^{0.66}$ is in line with $m_b^{0.75}$ found by Bergh et al. (10) and $m_b^{0.67}$ as suggested from the theory of similarity (3,21,44). Whether expressing $\dot{V}O_{2max}$ in relation to $m_b^{0.67}$ or $m_b^{0.75}$, it may not be critical as long as the unit approximates the theoretical value and not the traditional m_b. Considering the number of subjects in the present study and to avoid introducing yet another exponent, it seems reasonable to concur with the conclusions of Bergh et al. (10) and express $\dot{V}O_{2max}$ in relation to $m_b^{0.75}$, which has become quite common for evaluating running economy or to indicate the performance capacity of runners.

Previous reports of higher $\dot{V}O_{2max}$ for midfield players were not supported by the results of the present study. This may be a result of both higher movement demands of attack and defensive positions in modern soccer and the failure of previous studies to apply appropriate scaling for body mass differences. If defense players are consistently heavier compared with midfield and forward players, as found in the present study and by Davis et al. (14), the argument for using the expression $mL \cdot kg^{-0.75} \cdot min^{-1}$ becomes even stronger.

As no standardized protocol for testing strength of soccer players exists, it is difficult to compare results among different studies. In our view, commonly used isokinetic tests do not reflect the movement of the limbs involved during soccer. Tests employing free barbells will reflect the functional strength of the soccer player more accurately. Furthermore, free barbells are readily available to most teams and provide more teams the potential to develop a meaningful functional testing program in conjunction with strength training. In strength training studies, it has been observed that measured increases in strength are dependent on the similarities between training and testing exercise. This specificity in movement patterns in strength training probably reflects the role of learning and coordination (1,34). The neuromuscular system also reacts sensitively in terms of adaptation to slow or fast contraction stimuli (36,38). Increased peak torque has been observed at or near the velocity of training (8,9) and at speeds below training velocity (26). Nevertheless, in sports-specific training for high velocity movements, a combination of maximum strength training in a basic nonspecific movement with emphasis on high velocity and high mobilization of power, and training the fast movement in the same period of time, gave a substantially higher increase in movement velocity (24,43) than training the fast movement itself, even with supramaximal velocities (41). These findings question some of the fundamentals trying to establish both movement and velocity specificity as basics for strength development. Higher values for vertical jump height of defense and forward players compared with midfield players (Table 2) may be explained by the tendency for defense and forward players to be involved in more jumping and tackling compared with midfield players.

The values of the strength parameters in the present study are not high compared with other team sports such as football or handball (3). Considering maximal strength, from testing of other explosive events it would be reasonable to expect, for a 75-kg male, squat values higher than 200 kg (90° in the knee joint) or about 11.0 $kg \cdot m_b^{-0.67}$. The expected values for bench press would be 100 kg or about 5.5 $kg \cdot m_b^{-0.67}$. For vertical jump height, it would be reasonable to expect that the elite soccer player have values higher than 60 cm. A higher level of all strength parameters would be preferable and would reduce the risk for injuries and allow for more powerful jumps, kicks, tackles, and sprints among other factors. Both maximal strength and rate of force development are important factors in successful soccer players becasue of the demand on the organism that the situations in a game give, which should be considered while choosing regimens for maximal strength training. Such training regimens for maximal strength training involve few repetitions with high loads and high velocity of movement and are described thoroughly elsewhere (34,36).

In the present study, maximal strength was proportional to $m_b^{0.55}$ and $m_b^{0.74}$ for squats and bench press, respectively; i.e., maximal strength per kilogram of body mass displayed an inverse relationship to body mass. Considering the small number of subjects in the present study, we suggest that maximal strength in soccer players should be expressed in relation to $m_b^{0.67}$ as suggested from the theory of scaling (3). Absolute strength is important when attempting to move an external object such as the ball or an opponent. Strength relative to body mass is the important factor when carrying body weight, especially for acceleration and deceleration in the soccer play. Relative strength comparisons are not functionally representative when values are divided by body mass. If maximum strength is divided by body mass for comparative purposes, the heavier individual's capacity will be underestimated and not representative of on-field work capacity. This information is important for coaches and especially for evaluating physical fitness or work capacity in younger soccer players in different periods of growth where body weight and size differ significantly at the same age.

Values for Hb, Hct, *VC*, FEV_1/*VC*, and V_E in the present study were within the normal range of the male population (3) and not markedly different from values reported from studies of athletes by others (14,28,33).

CONCLUSIONS

The results of the present study support previous investigations indicating a relationship between endurance capacity, physical strength, and performance results in elite soccer.

Studying the results of $\dot{V}O_{2max}$, Rosenborg, theoretically, does have one player more on the field with a $\dot{V}O_{2max}$ of 77 $mL \cdot kg^{-1} \cdot min^{-1}$ (67.6–59.9 · 10 outfield players) compared with Strindheim. In addition, again theoretically, Rosenborg as a team manages to lift 296 kg more in squats compared with Strindheim (164.6–135.0 · 10 outfield players). Considering all the advantages of a high level of endurance and strength, as discussed above, these factors have high impact upon achievement of success in elite soccer. Neither $\dot{V}O_{2max}$ nor maximal strength comparison is functionally representative when values are divided by body mass. Therefore, it is concluded that, for soccer players, $\dot{V}O_{2max}$ should be expressed in relation to $m_b^{0.75}$ and maximal strength in relation to $m_b^{0.67}$. In the authors' opinion, further improvements in the level of play in soccer require greater emphasis on optimizing the functional strength and endurance capacity of the athletes. Superior technical and tactical ability in soccer can only be consistently demonstrated throughout the course of a 90-min competition by athletes with high endurance capacity and strength.

Address for correspondence: Ulrik Wisløff, Department of Physiology and Biomedical Engineering, Faculty of Medicine, Norwegian University of Science and Technology, N-7005 Trondheim, Norway. E-mail: Ulrik.wisloff@medisin.ntnu.no.

REFERENCES

1. ALMÅSBAKK, B. and J. HOFF. Coordination, determinant of velocity specificity? *J. Appl. Physiol.* 80:2046–2052, 1996.
2. APOR, P. Successful formulae for fitness training. In: *Science and Football*, T. Reilly, A. Less, K. Davids, and W. J. Murphy (Eds.). London: E. & F.N. Spon, 1988, pp. 95–107.
3. ÅSTRAND, P.-O. and K. RODAHL. *Textbook of Work Physiology*, New York: McGraw-Hill, 1986.
4. BALSOM, P. Evaluation of physical performance. In: *Football (Soccer)*. B. Ekblom (Ed.). London: Blackwell Scientific, 1994, pp. 102–123.
5. BANGSBO, J. and M. MIZUNO. Morphological and metabolic alterations in soccer players with detraining and retraining and their relation to performance. In: *Science and Football*, T. Reilly, A. Less, K. Davids, and W. J. Murphy (Eds), London: E. & F.N. Spon, 1988, pp. 114–124.
6. BANGSBO, J., L. NØRREGAARD, and F. THORSØE. Active profile of competition soccer. *Can. J. Sports Sci.* 16:110–116, 1991.
7. BANGSBO, J. Physiological demands. In: *Football (Soccer)*. B. Ekblom (Ed.). London: Blackwell Scientific, 1994, pp. 43–59.
8. BEHM, D. G. and D. G. SALE. Velocity specificity of resistance training. *Sports Med.* 15:374–388, 1993.
9. BEHM, D. G. and D. G. SALE. Intendent rather than actual movement velocity determines velocity-specific training response. *J. Appl. Physiol.* 74:359–368, 1993.
10. BERGH, U., B. SJØDIN, A. FORSBERG, and J. SVEDENHAG. The relationship between body mass and oxygen uptake during running in humans. *Med. Sci. Sports Exerc.* 23:205–211, 1991.
11. BÜHRLE, M. and D. SCHMIDTBLEICHER. Der einfluss von maximalkrafttraining auf die bewegungsschnelligkeit (The influence of maximum strength training on movement velocity). *Leistungssport* 7:3–10, 1977.
12. CABRI, J., E. DE PROFT, W. DUFOUR, and J. P. CLARYS. The relation between muscular strength and kick performance. In: *Science and Football*, T. Reilly, A. Less, K. Davis, and W. J. Murphy (Eds.). London: E. & F.N. Spon, 1988, pp. 106–153.
13. COSTILL, D. L. Carbohydrates for exercise: dietary demands for optimal performance. *Int. J. Sports. Med.* 9:1–18, 1988.
14. DAVIS, J. A., J. BREWER, and D. ATKIN. Pre-season physiological characteristics of English first and second division soccer players. *J. Sport Sci.* 10:541–547, 1992.
15. DE PROFT, E., J. CABRI, W. DUFOUR, and J. P. CLARYS. Strength training and kick performance in soccer players. In: *Science and Football*, T. Reilly, A. Less, K. Davis, and W. J. Murphy (Eds.). London: E. & F.N. Spon, 1988, pp. 108–113.
16. DEMPSEY, J. A., P. G. HANSON, and K. HENDERSON. Exercise induced arterial hypoxemia in healthy humans at sea level. *J. Appl. Physiol.* 355:161–175, 1984.
17. DOUGLAS, T. Physiological characteristics of elite soccer players. *Sports Med.* 16:80–96, 1993.
18. EKBLOM, B. Applied physiology of soccer. *Sports Med.* 3:50–60, 1986.
19. GAUFFIN, H., J. EKSTRAND, L. ARNESSON, and H. TROPP. Vertical jump performance in soccer players: a comparative study of two training programs. *J. Hum. Movement Studies* 16:159–176, 1989.
20. GREEN, S. Anthropometric and physiological characteristics of South Australian soccer players. *Aust. J. Sci. Med. Sport* 24:3–7, 1992.
21. GÜNTHER, B. Dimensional analysis and the theory of biological similarity. *Physiol. Rev.* 55:659–699, 1975.
22. HELGERUD, J., F. INGJER, and B. STRØMME. Sex differences in performance-matched marathon runners. *Eur. J. Appl. Physiol.* 61:433–439, 1990.
23. HELGERUD, J. Maximal oxygen uptake, anaerobic threshold and running economy in women with similar performances level in marathons. *Eur. J. Appl. Physiol.* 68:155–161, 1994.
24. HOFF, J. and B. ALMÅSBAKK. The effects of maximum strength training on throwing velocity and muscle strength in female team-handball players. *J. Strength Cond. Res.* 9:255–258, 1995.
25. MANGINE, R. E., F. R. NOYES, M. P. MULLEN, and S. D. BARBER. A physiological profile of the elite soccer athlete. *J. Orthop. Sports Physiol. Therapy* 12:147–152, 1990.
26. NARICI, M. V., G. S. ROI, L. LANDONI, A. E. MINETI, and P. CERRETELLI. Change in force, cross-sectional area and neural activation during strength training and detraining of the human quadriceps. *Eur. J. Appl. Physiol.* 59:310–319, 1989.
27. NOWACKI, P. E., D. Y. CAI, C. BUHL, and U. KRUMMELBEIN. Biological performance of German soccer players (professionals and juniors) tested by special ergometry and treadmill methods. In: *Science and Football*, T. Reilly, A. Less, K. Davis, and W. J. Murphy (Eds.). London: E. & F.N. Spon, 1988, pp. 145–157.
28. RAVEN, P., L. GETTMAN, M. POLLOCK, and K. COOPER. A physiological evaluation of professional soccer players. *Br. J. Sports Med.* 109:209–216, 1976.
29. REILLY, T. and V. THOMAS. Estimated daily energy expenditures of professional association. *Ergonomics* 22:541–548, 1979.
30. REILLY, T. Football. In: *Physiology of Sports*, T. Reilly, N. Secher, P. Snell, and C. Williams (Eds.), London: E. & F.N. Spon, 1990, pp. 371–425.
31. REILLY, T. Motion characteristics. In: *Football (Soccer)*, B. Ekblom (Ed.). London: Blackwell Scientific, 1994, pp. 31–43.
32. REILLY, T. Physiological profile of the player: In: *Football (Soccer)*, B. Ekblom (Ed.), Blackwell Scientific, 1994, pp. 78–95.
33. RHODES, E. C., R. E. MOSHER, D. C MCKENZIE, I. M. FRANKS, and J. E POTTS. Physiological profiles of the Canadian Olympic soccer team. *Can. J. Appl. Sport Sci.* 11:31–36, 1986.
34. SALE, D. Neural adaptation to strength training. In: *Strength and Power in Sport*, P. Komi (Ed.). London: Blackwell Scientific, 1992, pp. 249–265.
35. SALTIN, B. Metabolic fundamentals in exercise. *Med. Sci. Sports Exerc.* 5:137–146, 1973.
36. SCHMIDTBLEICHER, D. Training for power events. In: *Strength and Power in Sport*. P. Komi (Ed.). London: Blackwell Scientific, 1992, pp. 381–395.
37. SMAROS, G. Energy usage during a football match. In: *Proceedings of the 1st International Congress on Sports Medicine Applied to Football*, L. Vecchiet (Ed.). Rome, 1980, pp. 795–801.
38. TESH, P. A. Training for body building. In: *Strength and Power in Sport*, P. Komi (Ed.). London: Blackwell Scientific, 1992, pp. 370–380.
39. THOMAS, V. and T. REILLY. Fitness assessment of English League soccer players throughout the competitive season. *Br. J. Sports Med.* 13:103–109, 1979.
40. VAN GOOL, D., D. VAN GERVEN, and J. BOUTMANS. The physiological load imposed on soccer players during real match-play. In: *Science and Football*, T. Reilly, A. Less, K. Davis, and W. J. Murphy (Eds.), London: E. & F.N. Spon, 1988, pp. 51–59.
41. VAN MUIJEN, A. E., H. JORIS, H. C. G. KEMPER, and G. J. VAN INGEN SCHENAU. Throwing practice with different ball weights: effects on throwing velocity and muscle strength in female handball players. *Sports Train. Med. Rehabil.* 2:103–113, 1991.
42. VERSTAPPEN, F. and F. BOVENS. Interval testing with football players at a laboratory. *Science and Football*, 2:15–16, 1989.
43. VOIGT, M. and C. KLAUSEN. Changes in muscle strength and speed of an unloaded movement after various training programs. *Eur. J. Appl. Physiol.* 60:370–376, 1990.
44. WEIBEL, E. R. *The Pathway for Oxygen: Structure and Function in the Mammalian Respiratory System.* Cambridge, MA: Harvard University Press, 1984, pp. 339–411.
45. WHITE, J. E., T. M. EMERY, J. L. KANE, R. GROVES, and A. B. RISMAN. Pre-season fitness profiles of professional soccer players. In: *Science and Football*, T. Reilly, A. Less, K. Davis, and W. J. Murphy (Eds.), London: E. & F.N. Spon, 1988, pp. 164–171.
46. WILLIAMS, C., R. M. REID, and R. COUTTES. Observations on the aerobic power of university Rugby players and professional soccer players. *Br. J. Sports Med.* 7:390–391, 1973.
47. ZERNICKE, R. F. and B. J. LOITZ. In: *Football (Soccer)*, B. Ekblom (Ed.). London: Blackwell Scientific, 1994, pp. 77–95.

Maximal squat strength is strongly correlated to sprint performance in elite soccer players.

Ulrik Wisløff[1], Carlo Castagna[2], Jan Helgerud[1], and Jan Hoff[1]

[1]Department of Physiology and Biomedical Engineering, Norwegian University of Science and Technology, Faculty of Medicine, [2] University of Ancona, Italy.

Abstract

Strength is inherent in high level soccer play, but the relation between strength and sprint performance is discussed. The aim of this report is to establish whether maximal strength is correlated to sprint and jump performance in elite soccer players. Seventeen male international soccer players, 25.8±2.9 years, 177.3±4.1 cm and 76.5±7.6 kg were tested for maximal strength in half squats and sprinting abilities 0-30m, 20m shuttle run sprint and jumping height as well as maximal oxygen consumption. There was a correlation between maximal strength in half squats (165.6±24.5 kg) and 10m and 30m sprint, 1.88±0.3 sec and 4.10±0.20 sec respectively, as well as 20m shuttle run sprint and jumping height. Maximal oxygen uptake was 65.7±4.3 mL · kg^{-1} · min^{-1}. High squat strength performance did not imply a reduced level of maximal oxygen consumption in elite level soccer players.

Introduction

Male elite soccer player's covers 8-12 km during a game, depending on team-role (Bangsbo 1991; Reilly and Thomas 1976; Reilly 1996), nutritional status (Saltin 1973; Jacobs et al. 1982), and aerobic capacity (Smaros 1980; Helgerud et al. 2001). Within this aerobic context a sprint bout occurs every 90s (Reilly and Thomas 1976) lasting 2-4s (Reilly and Thomas 1976; Bangsbo 1991; O'Donoghue 2001). Sprinting constitute 1 to 11% of the total match-distance (Bangsbo, 1991; Reilly and Thomas 1976), corresponding to 0.5-3.0 % of effective play-time (Bangsbo 1991; O'Donoghue 2001; Ali and Farraly 1991; Bangsbo 1992). Recently we showed that improvement in aerobic capacity in elite junior soccer players increased the distance covered, the play intensity, number of sprints, and ball involvement during a game (Helgerud et al. 2001). These findings highlight some of the advantages of a high aerobic capacity in soccer, even if the most interesting parts of soccer involvement are characterized by high intensities.

During a game professional soccer players performs on about 50 turns sustaining forceful contractions to maintain balance and control of the ball against defensive pressure (Withers 1982). Thus, strength and power share importance with endurance in soccer play. Maximal strength is one basic quality that influences power performance. An increase in maximal strength is usually connected with an improvement in relative strength and therefore with improvement of power abilities. A significant relationship has been observed between 1RM and acceleration and movement velocity (Bührle and Schmidtbleicher 1977). This maximal strength/power performance relationship is supported by jump test results as well as in 30 m sprint results (Schmidtbleicher 1992; Hoff et al. 2001). By increasing the available force of muscular contraction in appropriate muscles or muscle groups, acceleration and speed in skills critical to soccer such as turning, sprinting, and changing pace may improve (Bangsbo et al. 1991).

The aim of this study was to access a thorough physical analysis of elite soccer players and determine the relationship between strength and dependent variables sprints and jumps.

Methods

Subjects

Seventeen male elite soccer players from Rosenborg FC (Trondheim, Norway) took part in the study. Rosenborg FC is the last-decade's most successful team of the Norwegian male elite soccer league winning the league 10 times in a row, and has recently gained international status, successfully competing in the Champions League UEFA tournament in 7 years in a row. The players studied were all full time professional soccer players and trained on a daily basis. The player's physical and physiological characteristic is presented in Table 1. Each subject reviewed and signed consent forms approved by the Human Research Review Committee prior to participating in the study.

Table 1. Physical and physiological characteristics of players

	Age (yrs)	Height (cm)	Mass (kg)	[Hb] ($g \cdot dl^{-1}$)	Hct (%)	VC (liters)	FEV_1 (liters)	FEV_1/VC (%)	f_{cmax} ($beats \cdot min^{-1}$)
Total (n=17)	25.8 ±2.9	177.3 ± 4.1	76.5 ± 7.6	16.0 ± 1.2	46.3 ± 2.3	5.6 ± 1.0	5.2 ± 0.8	92.9 ± 3.0	198 ± 17

Data are mean ± SD. [Hb]; hemoglobin concentration in blood, Hct; hematocrit, VC; vital capacity, FEV_1; forced expiratory volume in 1 second, $\dot{V}O_{2max}$; maximal oxygen uptake, f_{cmax}; maximal heart rate.

Day 1: Upon entering the laboratory, hemoglobin (Hb), hematocrit (Hct) and lung function were measured for normative data comparisons. For Hb and Hct determination, blood was drawn from a fingertip and analyzed immediately using the Refletron (Boehringer Manheim, Germany) and Ames microspin (Bayer Diagnostic, Germany) devices, respectively. Vital capacity (VC) and forced expiratory volume in one second (FEV_1) were determined using a flow screen (Jaeger, Germany). After these preliminary tests, subjects completed a 20 minutes warm-up at approximately 50-60 % of $\dot{V}O_{2max}$. Vertical jump height was determined using a force platform with a software specifically developed for the platform (Bioware, Kistler, Switzerland). Jumping height was determined as the center of mass displacement calculated from force development and measured body mass. Strength testing consisted of one repetition maximum of half squats (90° angle of the knee joints) performed with a competition standard Olympic style bar and weights (T-100G, Eleiko, Sweden). The players were familiar with half squats as part of their regular strength training programs.

After the strength tests each player ran for 10 minutes on a motorized treadmill (Challenger LE5000) at 50 - 60 % of VO_{2max} before measuring VO_{2max} and maximal heart rate (f_{cmax}). In our laboratory we routinely test VO_{2max} after the strength test and get similar VO_{2max} as when performing the treadmill test on a separate day (unpublished results). The specific procedure for VO_{2max} and f_{cmax} determination is routinely used and has been previously described (Helgerud et al. 1994). The speed of the treadmill was increased every minute to a level that brought the subject close to exhaustion after approximately 5 minutes. Inclination was constant at 3 degrees. Immediately after VO_{2max} determination, each subject ran for 2 minutes at an exercise intensity of 50 - 60 % of VO_{2max} directly followed by a supramaximal intensity run, resulting in exhaustion after ~3 minutes. Heart rate (f_c) was determined using short-range radio telemetry (Polar Sporttester, Polar Electro, Finland). The highest heart frequency during the last minute of the supraintensity run was recorded as f_{cmax}. Oxygen uptake (VO_2), minute ventilation (V_E) and breathing frequency (f_b) were measured during work using an Ergo Oxyscreen (Jaeger EOS sprint, Germany).

Day 2: Three days after the test of aerobic capacity, vertical jump height, and maximal strength, a 30-meter sprint test, and a 20-meter shuttle run-test (MSR) were performed after 30 minutes of thorough warm-up. The tests were performed on an indoor handball field with a parquet floor. Time was recorded by photocells (Brower Timing, USA). Each subject carried out 2 trials in each sprint test separated by 5 minutes of rest. When ready to sprint, the subjects decided themselves when to start the sprint test from a static position, with the time being recorded when the subjects intercepted the photocell beam.

Allometric scaling.

Comparisons between athletes of capacities like VO_{2max} and maximal strength (1RM) are often made in terms of absolute measures ($L \cdot min^{-1}$ or kg) or relative to body weight ($mL \cdot kg^{-1} \cdot min^{-1}$) or ($kg \cdot kgbw^{-1}$) both of which are very routine and functionally imprecise. The oxygen cost of running at a standard velocity does not increase in direct proportion to body mass in trained individuals, and similarly strength does not increase in direct proportion to body mass. Dimensional scaling suggest that comparisons between a small and a bigger individual should be expressed by kg bodyweight raised to the power of 0.67 as $mL \cdot kg^{-1} \cdot min^{-1}$ or $kg \cdot kgbw^{-1}$ (Åstrand and Rodahl 1986; Helgerud 1994, Wisløff et al 1998). Based on descriptive data Helgerud (1994) found that comparisons of VO_{2max} should be expressed relative to body mass raised to the power of 0.75 when running. If dimensional scaling is not used, both relative strength and relative endurance will underestimate the big athlete and overestimate the small one (Wisløff et al 1998).

Statistical analyses

Data are presented as mean ± SD. For comparison of unrelated observations we used the Kruskal-Wallis test including appropriate procedures for multiple comparisons between groups. Pearson' product-moment correlation were used to determine the relations between selected parameters. $P < 0.05$ was considered statistically significant.

Results

The results from VO_{2max}, squats, vertical jump height and 30-meter sprint test is presented in Table 2.

Table 2. Results from test of VO_{2max}, 1RM squat, vertical jump height and 30-m sprint

	VO_{2max}			Squats		
	$l \cdot min^{-1}$	$ml \cdot kg^{-1} \cdot min^{-1}$	$ml \cdot kg^{-0.75} \cdot min^{-1}$	(kg)	$(kg \cdot m_b^{-1})$	$(kg \cdot m_b^{-0.67})$
Total (n=17)	5.0 ± 0.4	65.7 ± 4.3	194 ± 10	171.7 ± 21.2	2.2 ± 0.3	9.4 ± 1.5

Data are mean ± SD. VO_{2max}, maximal oxygen uptake; 1RM, one repetition maximum.

Vertical jump	Sprint		
(cm)	10 m	20 m	30 m
56.4 ± 4.0	1.82 ± 0.3	3.0 ± 0.3	4.0 ± 0.2

The level of 1RM correlated well with 10 meter sprint time ($r=0.94$, $p<0.001$, Figure 1A), 30 meter sprint time ($r=0.71$, $p<0.01$, Figure 1B), 10 meter shuttle run ($r=0.68$, $p<0.02$, Figure 1C) and jumping height ($r=0.78$, $p<0.02$, Figure 1D).

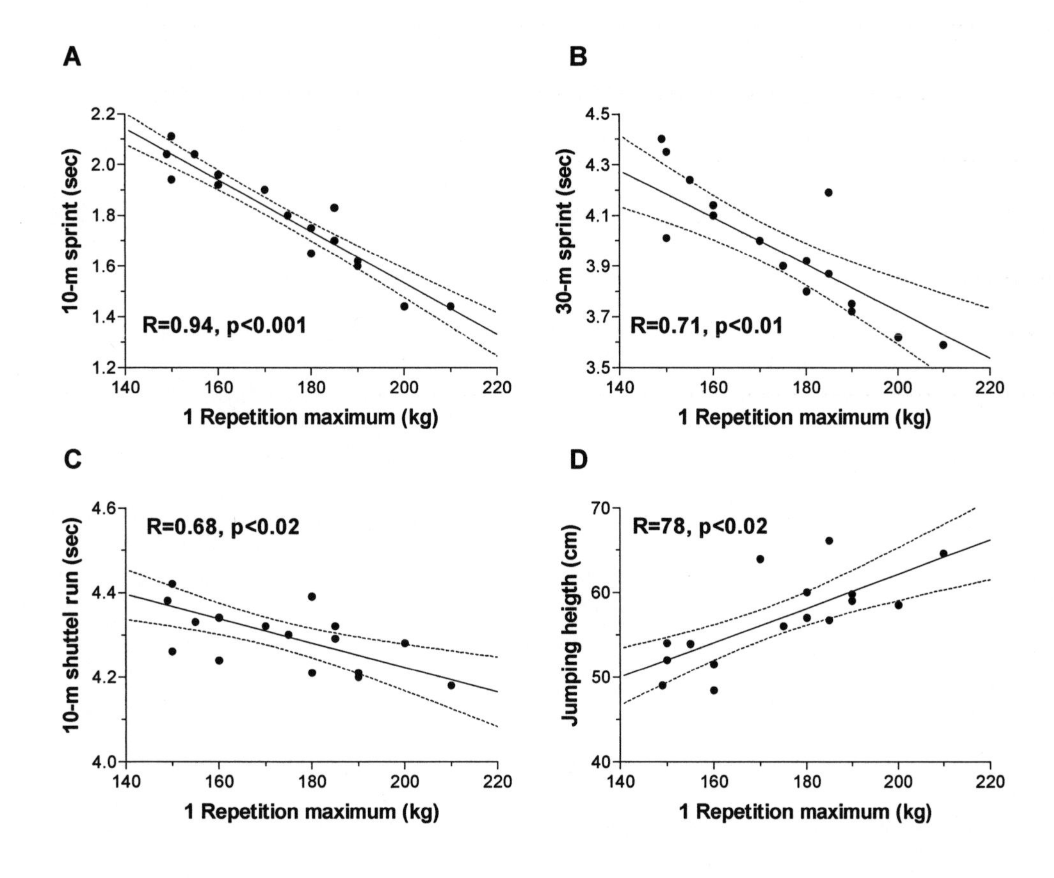

Figure 1. Correlation between 1 Repetition Maximum and sprint and jumping performance.

No positional differences were observed among players, and average results are therefore presented.

Discussion

A strong correlation exists between maximal strength and sprint performance. The highest correlations should be expected where the acceleration is the highest, according to Newtons 2nd law of motion. There are however strong correlations between maximal strength and all sprint tests, also including both 20 - 30m performance, where the acceleration is substantially smaller than for 0 – 10m, and the 20m shuttle run test, where braking the velocity is part of the performance.

It should be noted though that in Rosenborg FC the strength training was performed on individual basis without any supervised training regimen from the coach. However, all players performed half squats as a part of their strength-training regimen. Nine of the players were students and got advise from our research group and performed a strength-training regimen twice a week using few repetitions with high loads and high velocity of movement as described below. These nine players had considerably higher values of 1RM compared to the other 8 players. It is important to underline the emphasis on maximal mobilization of concentric force in this training regimen. We have recently showed the effectiveness of such training program, by increasing 1RM in half squats about 35 % (from 160 kg to 215 kg): 5 repetition · 4 series, 2 times per week in 8 weeks. Every time the player manages to perform 5 repetition in the last series, the load should be increased by 5 kg the next training session (Hoff 2001). A higher level of maximal strength and power in the "high strength" group are supposed to result in more powerful jumps, kicks, tackles and sprints and reduce the risk for injuries. As several of the players had undergone a training regime with emphasis on maximal mobilization of force, that normally result in high training effects on rate of force development, might mean that the correlation between maximal strength and all sprint and jump parameters are not a global finding. If other training regimens for improving maximal strength are used as background for enhanced strength, the correlation to sprinting and jumping performance might be different.

As no standardized protocol for testing strength of soccer players exists, it is difficult to compare results among different studies. In our view, commonly used isokinetic tests do not reflect the movement of the limbs involved during soccer. Tests employing free barbells will reflect the functional strength of the soccer player more accurately. Furthermore, free barbells are readily available to most teams and provide more teams the potential to develop a meaningful functional testing program in conjunction with strength training. The result from 1RM half squats in this study is in line with previous studies using free barbells (Wisløff et al. 1998; Hoff 2002; Helgerud et al. 2001).

Both maximal strength and rate of force development are important factors in successful soccer players because of the demand on the organism that the situations in a game give. This should be considered while choosing regimens for maximal strength training. Such training regimens for maximal strength training involve few repetitions with high loads and high velocity of contraction, and are described thoroughly elsewhere (Sale 1992; Schmidtbleicher 1992, Almåsbakk & Hoff 1996, Hoff & Almåsbakk 1995, Hoff et al. 2002). The positive relationship between maximal strength and vertical jump height and 30-meter sprint is in accordance with previous studies (Hoff and Almåsbakk 1995; Bührle and Scmidtbleicher 1977; Schmidtbleicher 1992). Vertical jump height was in line with previous reports on elite soccer players (Wisløff et al. 1998; Hoff 2002).

Recent studies reports that 96% of sprint bouts are shorter than 30m (Valquer et al. 1998), and 49% less than 10m. This should be kept in mind when choosing a test regimen. The 30-meter sprint times reported here are in line with other studies of elite soccer players (Hoff 2002, Helgerud 2001). Split times gives important information, and our data show that there are substantial differences within the 30m test. Two of the players showing similar performance on the 30m test, show great differences in the first and in the last part of the 30m, and should subsequently be suggested different training regimen.

The present shuttle-run sprint-test involved a keen change of direction that stressed balance, strength, flexibility and braking and acceleration capacity of players. Observing no relationship between 20MSRT and the 30-meter sprint test are in line with previous studies (Young 2001; Buttifant et al. 1999). However, both sprint capacities are of importance in soccer and the present data shows that both capacities should be included and evaluated in a sprint test-battery of soccer players.

As reported in previous studies (Apor 1988; Wisløff et al. 1998) high ranked teams have quite high level of VO_{2max}. VO_{2max} of about 65.7 mL · kg^{-1} · min^{-1} or 194 mL · kg$^{-0.75}$ · min^{-1} is in line with a recent study from the same team (Wisløff et al. 1998), and in Spanish Liga soccer players (Casajus 2001). In activities that involve dynamic work with large muscle mass, as in soccer, it is generally assumed that VO_{2max} is primarily limited by maximal cardiac output (Wagner 1992). Interval training with a working intensity between 90-95 % of maximal heart rate primarily increases the maximal cardiac output. We have recently showed the effectiveness of such training program, increasing VO_{2max} about 5 mL · kg^{-1} · min^{-1} by interval training, 4 · 4 minutes intervals, 2 times per week, in 8 weeks in well trained elite junior soccer players (Helgerud et al. 2001). This lead to several positive on-field adaptations such as increased distance covered, intensity of play, number of sprints performed and ball involvement's, highlighting some of the advantages of increasing VO_{2max} in soccer players. The results in this group of players showed that a high level of maximal strength did not compromise a high level of VO_{2max}.

That endurance training inhibits or interferes with strength development is concluded in several studies (Chromiak and Mulvaney 1990; Dudley and Djamil 1985; Hennessy and Watson 1994; Hickson 1980). Nelson et al. (1990) claimed that simultaneous training of strength and endurance inhibits the normal adaptation to either training regimen when performed alone. A more interesting question for the soccer players is how maximal strength training affects the endurance performance because both capacities are needed. The fact that there was a trend for the high-strength group to have the highest VO_{2max} compared with the low-strength group contradict previous findings. Thus up to a reasonable high level of both strength- and endurance capacity there seem to be little interference of training strength and endurance capacity simultanously, which obviously have to be carried out in soccer, since both capacities are needed.

Rosenborg FC organize most of the endurance training purely as playing sessions and reach satisfactory results this way. Whether endurance training should be organized as playing-sessions, or pure running, must be considered by each team. It seems, however, in small-sided play to exist a ceiling effect around 65 mL · kg^{-1} · min^{-1}, whereas no such effect exist in running (Hoff et al. 2002). Recently we showed that interval training with the ball might be as effective as pure uphill running (which normally is required to get high enough exercise intensity) when performed either in a dribbling-track or as supervised play-session (Hoff et al. 2002). Monitoring the training intensity during a playing session, with the assistance of a heart rate monitor, will be helpful in this regard.

Conclusions

Maximal strength in half squats determines the sprint performance in high level soccer players in this team. The strong correlations are evident in all aspects of 0-30m sprints as well as the 20m shuttle run test and jumping height. The high strength players in this team had used a training regime with few repetitions, high loads and emphasis on maximal mobilisation of force in the concentric part of the half squat. High strength half squat performance does not imply a lower level of oxygen consumption in elite players.

References

Ali, A., and M.Farrally. (1991) A computer-video aided time-motion analysis technique for match analysis. *J Sports Med Phys Fit*, 1991, 31:82-88.

Almaasbakk, B. & Hoff,J., (1996), Coordination, the determinant of velocity specificity, *J Appl Physiol*, 80(5): 2046-2052

Apor, P. Successful formulae for fitness training. In: Science and Football. A.L. Reilly T., K. Davids, and W.J. Murphy, eds. E. F.& Spon: London, New York, 1988. pp. 95-107.

Baker, D., S. Nance. The relation between strength and power in professional rugby league players. *J. Strength Cond Res*, 13:224-229. 1999.

Bangsbo, J., L. Nørregaard, and Thorsøe F. Activity profile of competition soccer. *Can J Sport Sci*:110-116. 1991.

Bangsbo, J. Time and motion characteristics of competiton soccer. *Science and Football*:34-40. 1992.

Bangsbo, J. Fitness training in football, a scientific approach. Copenhagen, Denmark: HO+Storm, 2880 Bagsvaer, 1993.

Bangsbo, J. Physiological demands. In: Football (Soccer). B. Ekblom (Ed.) Blackwell Scientific Publications, London, 1994, pp. 43-59.

Behm, D. G. and D.G. Sale. Velocity specificity of resistance training. *Sports Med.* 15: 374-388, 1993.

Behm, D. G. and D.G. Sale. Intendent rather than actual movement velocity determines velocity-specific training response. *J. Appl. physiol.* 74: 359-368, 1993.

Bergh U., Sjødin B., Forsberg A. and Svedenhag J. (1991) The relationship between body mass and oxygen uptake during running in humans. *Med Sci Sports Exerc* 23:205-211

Bührle, M. and D. Schmidtbleicher. Der einfluss von maximalkrafttraining auf die bewegungsschnelligkeit (The influence of maximum strength training on movement velocity). *Leistungssport*, 7: 3-10, 1977.

Buttifant, D., Graham K., Cross K. Agility and speed of soccer players are two different performance parameters. *J. Sports Sci.* 17:809. 1999.

Cometti, G., N.A. Maffiuletti, M. Pousson, J.C. Chatard, N. Maffulli. Isokinetic strength and anaerobic power of elite, subelite and amateur French soccer players. *Int. J. Sports Med.* 22:45-51. 2001.

Delecluse, C.H., H. Van Coppenolle, E. Willems, R. Diles, M. Goris, M. Van Leemputte, and M. Vuylsteke. Analysis of of 100 meter sprint performance as a multi-dimensional skill. *J. Hum. Mov. Stud.*:87-101. 1995.

Delecluse, C.H., H. Van Coppenolle, E. Willems, M. Van Leemputte R. Diles, and M. Goris. Influence of high-resistance and high-velocity training on sprint performance. *Med. Sci. Sports Exerc.* 27:1-7. 1995.

Dudley G.A. and Djamil R. (1985) Incompatibility of endurance- and strength-training modes of exercise. *J Appl Physiol* 59:1446-1451

Ekblom, B. Appied physiology of soccer. *Sports Med*:50-60. 1986.

Föhrenbach, R., W. Hollmann, A. Mader, W. Thiele. Testverfahren und metabolisch orientiere intensitätssteuerung im Sprinttraining mit submaximaler Belastungsstruktur. *Leistungssport*:15-24. 1986.

Gambetta, V. How to develop sport-specific speed. *Sports Coach.* 19:22-24. 1996.

Helgerud, J. Maximal oxygen uptake, anaerobic threshold and running economy in women and men with similar performances level in marathons. *Eur J Appl Physiol.* 68: 155-161, 1994.

Hennessy L.C. and Watson A.W. (1994) The interference effects of training for strength and endurance simultaneously. *J Strength Cond Res* 8(1):12-19, 1994.

Hickson R.D., Rosenkoetter M.A and Brow M.M. Strength training effects on aerobic power and short term endurance. *Med Sci Sports Exerc* 12: 336-339, 1980.

Helgerud, J., L.C. Engen, U. Wisløff, and J. Hoff. Aerobic endurance training improves soccer performance. *Med. Sci. Sports Exerc.* 33:1925-1931. 2001.

Hoff, J., G.O.Berdahl, S. Bråten. Jumping height development and body weight considerations in ski jumping. In: Science and Skiing II, Müller, E., H. Schwameder, C. Raschner, S. Lidinger, E. Kornexl (eds), Verlag Dr. Kovac, Hamburg, 403-412, 2001.

Hoff, J. Training for rate of force development enhances running economy and aerobic performance. *Med Sci Sports Exerc.* 33: 5 Suppl, S270, 2001.

Hoff, J., J. Helgerud, U.Wisløff. Endurance training into the next millenium; Muscular strength training effects on aerobic endurance performance. *Am J Med Sports*, 4:58-67, 2002.

Hoff, J. and B. Almåsbakk. The effects of maximum strength training on throwing velocity and muscle strength in female team-handball players. *J. Strength Cond. Res.* 9: 255-258, 1995.

Hoff, J., U. Wisløff, L.C. Engen, O.J. Kemi, J. Helgerud. Soccer specific aerobic endurance training. *Br J Sports Med*, 36: 218-221, 2002.

Jacobs, I., N. Westlin, J. Karlsson, M. Rasmusson, and B. Houghton. Muscle glycogen and diet in elite soccer players. *Eur J Appl Physiol*:297-302. 1982.

Kollath, E., and Quade K. Measurement of sprinting speed of professional and amateur soccer players. In: Science and Football II. J.C.a.A.S. T. Reilly. E & FN Spon: London, 1993. pp. 31-36.

Narici, M.V., G.S. Roi, L. Landoni, A.E. Mineti, and P. Cerretelli. Change in force, cross-sectional area and neural activation during strength training and detraining of the human quadriceps. *Eur. J. Appl. Physiol.* 59: 310-319, 1989.

Nelson, A.G., D.A. Arnall, S.F. Loy, L.J. Silvester, and R.K. Conlee. Consequences of combining strength and endurance regimens. *Phys. Ther.,* 70: 287-294, 1990.

O'Donoghue, P. Time-motion analysis of work rate in elite soccer. In: Notational analysis of sport IV. M.H.a.F. Tavares. Centre for team sports studies, Faculty of Sport Sciences and Physical Education, University of Porto, Portugal: Porto, 2001. pp. 65-70.

Parsons, L.S., and M.T. Jones. Development of speed, agility and quickness for tennis athletes. *J Strength Cond Res*:14-19. 1998.

Reilly, T., and Thomas V. A motion analysis of work-rate in different positional roles in professional football match-play. *J. Hum. Mov Stud.* :87-97. 1976.

Reilly, T. Motion analysis and physiological demands. In: Science and Soccer. R. T. E & FN Spon: London, 1996. pp. 65-79.

Rienzi, E., Drust B, Reilly T., Carter J.E.L., Martin A. Investigation of the anthropometric and work-rate profiles of elite South American international soccer players. *J Sports Med Phys Fitness*. 40:162-169. 2000.

Sale, D.G. Neural adaptations to strength training. In: Strength and power in sport. P.V. Komi (Ed.) Blackwell Scientific Publications, 1992, pp. 249-265.

Saltin, B. Metabolic fundamentals in exercise. *Med Sci Sports Exerc*:137-146. 1973.

Schmidtbleicher, D. Training for power events. In: Strength and power in sport. P. Komi (Ed.) Blackwell Scientific Publications, London, 381-395, 1992.

Smaros, G. Energy usage during football match. In: Proceedings of the first international congress on sports medicine applied to football. L. Vecchiet. : Rome, 1980. pp. 795-801.

Soares, J.M.C. Fitness testing in soccer. In: W. Spinks. University of Technology, Sydney: Sydney, 1999. p. 17.

Tumilty, D. Protocols for the physiological assessment of male and female soccer players. In: Physiological testing of elite athelete. Champaign IL: Human Kinetics Publishers, 2000. pp. 1-16.

Valquer, W., Barros T.L., Sant'anna M. High intensity motion pattern analyses of Brazilian elite soccer players. In: IV World Congress of Notational Analysis of Sport. H.M. Tavares Fernanado. FCDEF-UP: Porto, Portugal, 1998. p. 80.

Van Muijen, A.E., H. Joris, H.C.G. Kemper, and G.J. Van Ingen Schenau. Throwing practice with different ball weights: Effects on throwing velocity and muscle strength in female handball players. *Sports Train. Med. Rehab.* 2: 103-113, 1991.

Voigt, M. and C. Klausen. Changes in muscle strength and speed of an unloaded movement after various training programs. *Eur. J. Appl. Physiol.* 60: 370-376, 1990.

Wagner PD., New ideas on limitations to VO_{2max}. *Exerc Sport Sci Review*, 1: 10-14, 2000.

Wisløff, U., J. Helgerud, and J. Hoff. Strength and endurance of elite soccer players. *Med. Sci. Sports Exerc.* 30:462-467. 1998.

Withers, R.T. Match analyses of Australian professional soccer players. *J Human Movement Studies.* 8:159-176. 1982.

Young, W., B. McClean, AND J. Ardagna. Relationship between strength qualities and sprinting performance. *J. Sports Med. Phys. Fit.*:13-19. 1995.

Young, W.B., M.H. McDowell, B.J. Scarlett. Specificity of sprint and agility training methods. *J. Strength Cond Res.* 15:315-319. 2001.

Aerobic endurance training improves soccer performance

JAN HELGERUD, LARS CHRISTIAN ENGEN, ULRIK WISLØFF, and JAN HOFF

Norwegian University of Science and Technology, Department of Sport Sciences, N-7491 Trondheim, NORWAY

ABSTRACT

HELGERUD, J., L. C. ENGEN, U. WISLØFF, and J. HOFF. Aerobic endurance training improves soccer performance. *Med. Sci. Sports Exerc.*, Vol. 33, No. 11, 2001, pp. 1925–1931. **Purpose:** The aim of the present study was to study the effects of aerobic training on performance during soccer match and soccer specific tests. **Methods:** Nineteen male elite junior soccer players, age 18.1 ± 0.8 yr, randomly assigned to the training group ($N = 9$) and the control group ($N = 10$) participated in the study. The specific aerobic training consisted of interval training, four times 4 min at 90–95% of maximal heart rate, with a 3-min jog in between, twice per week for 8 wk. Players were monitored by video during two matches, one before and one after training. **Results:** In the training group: a) maximal oxygen uptake ($\dot{V}O_{2max}$) increased from 58.1 ± 4.5 mL·kg^{-1}·min^{-1} to 64.3 ± 3.9 mL·kg^{-1}·min^{-1} ($P < 0.01$); b) lactate threshold improved from 47.8 ± 5.3 mL·kg^{-1}·min^{-1} to 55.4 ± 4.1 mL·kg^{-1}·min^{-1} ($P < 0.01$); c) running economy was also improved by 6.7% ($P < 0.05$); d) distance covered during a match increased by 20% in the training group ($P < 0.01$); e) number of sprints increased by 100% ($P < 0.01$); f) number of involvements with the ball increased by 24% ($P < 0.05$); g) the average work intensity during a soccer match, measured as percent of maximal heart rate, was enhanced from 82.7 ± 3.4% to 85.6 ± 3.1% ($P < 0.05$); and h) no changes were found in maximal vertical jumping height, strength, speed, kicking velocity, kicking precision, or quality of passes after the training period. The control group showed no changes in any of the tested parameters. **Conclusion:** Enhanced aerobic endurance in soccer players improved soccer performance by increasing the distance covered, enhancing work intensity, and increasing the number of sprints and involvements with the ball during a match. **Key Words:** $\dot{V}O_{2max}$, LACTATE THRESHOLD, RUNNING ECONOMY, SKILL

Soccer is one of the most widely played and complex sports in the world, where players need technical, tactical, and physical skills to succeed. However, studies to improve soccer performance have often focused on technique and tactics at the expense of physical resources such as endurance, strength, and speed.

The average work intensity, measured as percent of maximal heart rate (f_{cmax}), during a 90-min soccer match is close to the lactate threshold (LT), or 80–90% of f_{cmax} (18). However, expressing intensity as an average over 90 min could result in a substantial loss of specific information. Indeed, soccer matches have periods and situations of high-intensity activity where accumulation of lactate takes place. Therefore, the players need periods of low-intensity activity to remove lactate from the working muscles.

A significant correlation between maximal oxygen uptake ($\dot{V}O_{2max}$) and distance covered during a match was found (20,22). Moreover, the finding that the rank among the best four teams in the Hungarian top soccer division was the same as the rank among their average $\dot{V}O_{2max}$ (2) strengthens the correlation between $\dot{V}O_{2max}$ and performance. This assumption is also supported by the results of Wisløff et al. (24), demonstrating a significant difference in $\dot{V}O_{2max}$ between the top team and a lower placed team in the Norwegian elite division.

A professional soccer player should ideally be able to maintain a high level of intensity throughout the whole game. Some studies, however, have shown a reduction in distance covered, a lower fractional work intensity, reduced f_c, reduced blood sugar levels, and reduced lactate levels in the second half of games compared with the first half (8). In determining aerobic endurance, $\dot{V}O_{2max}$ is considered the most important element. Other important determinants are LT and running economy (gross oxygen cost of running per meter (C_R)) (17). LT is the highest workload, oxygen consumption or heart frequency in dynamic work using large muscle groups, where production and elimination of lactate balances (10). In endurance sports, LT might be a better indicator of aerobic endurance performance than $\dot{V}O_{2max}$ (9). LT might also change without changes in $\dot{V}O_{2max}$, and a higher LT means, theoretically, that a player could maintain a higher average intensity in an activity without accumulation of lactate (10). Costill et al. (6) and Helgerud et al. (9), among others, have shown between-individual variations in C_R. The causes of variability are not well understood, but it seems likely that anatomical traits, mechanical/neuromuscular skills, and storage of elastic energy are important factors (17). Better C_R among well-trained runners compared with recreational runners are documented (9,10). C_R is normally expressed as oxygen consumption ($\dot{V}O_2$) at a standardized workload or $\dot{V}O_2$ per meter when running (7,9). Hoff et al. (13) have shown that aerobic

0195-9131/01/3311-1925/$3.00/0
MEDICINE & SCIENCE IN SPORTS & EXERCISE®

Submitted for publication October 2000.
Accepted for publication February 2001.

TABLE 1. Physical and physiological characteristics of players (± SD).

N	Age (yr)	Height (cm)	Mass (kg)	[Hb] ($g \cdot dL^{-1}$)	Hct (%)	VC (L)	FEV_1/VC (%)
19	18.1 (0.8)	181.3 (5.6)	72.2 (11.1)	14.3 (1.1)	43.7 (1.6)	5.14 (0.88)	88.5 (3.2)

[Hb], hemoglobin concentration in blood; Hct, hematocrit; VC, vital capacity; FEV_1, forced expiratory volume in 1 s.

performance can be increased by improving C_R with a strength training regimen, without affecting $\dot{V}O_{2max}$ or LT.

Several studies describe the physiological, tactical, and technical parameters during a soccer match, which characterize players at different levels (4,24). Cross-sectional studies show a correlation between $\dot{V}O_{2max}$ and these selected parameters (20,22); however, the basic question is whether this is a cause-and-effect phenomenon. Intervention studies concerning the effect of improving aerobic endurance on soccer performance have not, to date, been reported.

This study was carried out to evaluate the effects of a training protocol, aimed to improve aerobic endurance, on soccer performance. The hypothesis was that increased aerobic endurance can improve distance covered, work intensity, number of sprints, and number of involvements with the ball during a soccer match.

METHODS

Two Norwegian junior men elite teams, Nardo and Strindheim, took part in the study. The subjects had been playing soccer for more than 8 yr. Both teams had been among the most successful teams in Norway for the last 5 yr. Six of the players tested were members of the Norwegian national junior team. Players within each team were randomly assigned into either a training group (TG, $N = 9$) or a control group (CG, $N = 10$), so that each team had members in both groups. In repeated determination of $\dot{V}O_{2max}$ on the same subject, the standard deviation is 3%, including both biological and methodological variables (3). The actual number of subjects in the present study thus permitted detection of a 4.5% difference between groups ($P = 0.05$, power $= 0.90$). Each subject reviewed and signed consent forms approved by the Human Research Review Committee before the study. The subjects were only informed how to perform the physical and physiological tests; no information was given about the video analysis during the games. The head coaches spent equal time with their subjects in the TG and the CG. The athletes were truly unaware of the tested hypothesis. The physical and physiological characteristics of the subjects are presented in Table 1.

Training protocol. The aerobic training intervention consisted of interval training, consisting of four times 4 min each of running at an exercise intensity of 90–95% of f_{cmax} for each player, separated by periods of 3 min jogging at 50–60% of f_{cmax}. The interval training was administered as an extension of the regular training, twice per week over an 8-wk period in the beginning of the season. A regular week of training consisted of four times 1.5 h of practice and one game. Technical, tactical, strength, and sprint training were performed. About 1 h of each practice was organized as playing sessions in both teams. Endurance training was organized purely as part of these playing sessions. No extra strength training was performed. When the TG carried out interval training, the CG performed extra technical training such as heading drills, practicing free kicks, and exercises related to receiving the ball and changing direction.

Measurements. All players within a given team were tested on the same day, and the tests were performed in the same order. When entering the laboratory, hemoglobin (Hb), hematocrit (Hct), and lung function were measured for normative data comparisons. For Hb and Hct determination, blood was drawn from a fingertip and analyzed immediately using the Refletron (Boehringer Mannheim, Frankfurt, Germany) and Ames microspin (Bayer Diagnostic, Munich, Germany) devices, respectively. Vital capacity (VC) and forced expiratory volume in 1 s (FEV_1) were determined using a flow screen (Hoechberg, Germany). After these preliminary tests, subjects completed a 20-min warm-up at approximately 50–60% of $\dot{V}O_{2max}$. Vertical jump height was determined using a force platform with software specifically developed for the platform (BioWare, Kistler Instrumente AG, Winterthur, Switzerland). Jumping height was determined as the center of mass displacement calculated from force development and measured body mass. Strength testing consisted of one repetition maximum of bench press and of squats (90° angle of the knee joints) repetition performed with a competition standard Olympic style bar and weights (T-100G, Eleiko Sport, Halmstad, Sweden).

A 40-m sprint test, a technical test, and a test of maximal kicking velocity followed the strength tests. The time for the first test was measured using photocells (Brower Timing Systems, South Draper, UT) at the start, at 10 m, and at 40 m. Each subject had two trials separated by 5 min of rest. When ready to sprint, the subjects decided themselves when to start the sprint test from a static position, with the time being recorded when the subjects intercepted the photocell beam. The technical test was performed using 10 Select senior balls with an air pressure of 0.8 bar. The balls were placed 16 m from a goal, which was in turn divided into five zones. If the ball was kicked into the 50-cm-wide center zone it was worth 3 points, 2 points if it was placed into an inner zone 25 cm each side of the center zone, and 1 point if placed into an outer zone reaching an additional 25 cm out from the inner second zone. The subject was given 1 min to use his "preferential foot" to get the highest score possible. The technical test was repeated immediately after the $\dot{V}O_{2max}$ test to verify fatiguing effect on technical skills. Measurement of maximal kicking velocity was performed using a Panasonic (Tokyo, Japan) Wv-F350 E video camera recorded at 50 Hz. The subject was free to decide the length of the in-run. A centimeter scale was mounted on the wall parallel to the direction of the shot, giving the opportunity to calculate the speed of the ball as a fraction of the distance covered on the video picture. Each player was given two trials. The best trial was used in the data handling.

Following the strength, sprint, and technical tests, LT and $\dot{V}O_{2max}$ were determined during treadmill running at 3° inclination. The protocol used for measuring LT and $\dot{V}O_{2max}$ has been described previously (10). Briefly, LT determination began with a 10-min warm-up at 50–60% of $\dot{V}O_{2max}$, followed by measurement of baseline blood lactate concentration ($[la^-]_b$). LT was taken as the power output, $\dot{V}O_2$, or f_c that gave a $\Delta[la^-]_b$ of 1.5 $mmol \cdot L^{-1}$ above baseline using 5-min work bouts during a continuous, graded protocol. Subjects performed 5-min exercise stages progressing in intensity between 60 and 95% of $\dot{V}O_{2max}$. Running speed was increased by 1 $km \cdot h^{-1}$ at each stage, after a 20-s pause for blood sampling from a fingertip. The above-described protocol for LT was derived from a previous study (10). Values for running speed, $\dot{V}O_2$, f_c, and $[la^-]_b$ were recorded during a series of running sessions. Each test was performed at constant speed over a period of 20 min, and on separate days. The highest exercise intensity during the constant speed tests, where the $[la^-]_b$ increased < 1 $mmol \cdot L^{-1}$ during the last 15 min, was then defined as LT. The values from the constant speed tests were then compared with values from the graded tests. From the results of these studies, it was concluded that LT, using the graded protocol, was reached at a $\dot{V}O_2$ that gave on average $[la^-]_b$ 1.5 $mmol \cdot L^{-1}$ (ranging from 1.3–1.7 $mmol \cdot L^{-1}$) higher than those found immediately after the warm-up period.

After measuring LT, treadmill speed was increased to a level that brought the subject to $\dot{V}O_{2max}$ and to exhaustion after about 3 min. C_R was calculated at LT, the maximal exercise intensity at which it has been shown that a reliable relationship exists between intensity and $\dot{V}O_2$ (9). The highest f_c during the last minute was taken as f_{cmax}, measured by short-range radio telemetry (Polar Sporttester, Polar Electro, Finland). $\dot{V}O_2$, maximal minute ventilation ($\dot{V}_E$), respiratory exchange ratio (R), and breathing frequency were measured during each exercise stage using an Ergo Oxyscreen (Jaeger EOS sprint, Germany). Unhemolyzed blood lactate $[la^-]_b$ was determined using a YSI Model 1500 Sport Lactate Analyzer (Yellow Springs Instrument Co., Yellow Springs, OH).

$\dot{V}O_{2max}$ expressed as $mL \cdot kg^{-1} \cdot min^{-1}$ implies linearity between oxygen uptake and body mass, which is not the case (5). When expressing $\dot{V}O_{2max}$ as $mL \cdot kg^{-1} \cdot min^{-1}$, light individuals are overestimated in terms of work capacity (e.g., endurance athletes) and heavy individuals are underestimated. The opposite is true when evaluating oxygen cost of running at submaximal workloads. Consequently, Wisløff et al. (24), Helgerud (9), and Bergh et al. (5) have concluded that when comparisons among people of different body mass are made for running, oxygen uptake should be expressed as $mL \cdot kg^{-0.75} \cdot min^{-1}$.

Video analysis. Players were monitored by a video system during two regular games, played on a neutral field, before and after the training period. During games, f_c was measured using a heart rate monitor (Polar Sporttester). The f_c measurements were divided into different intensity zones on the basis of percent f_{cmax}: < 70%, 70–85%, 85–90%, 90–95%, and > 95%. Time spent in different intensity zones was calculated. Because of injuries, data were collected on eight subjects in both groups. All games were played on a high-quality indoor field consisting of artificial curled nylon grass filled with sand. Video recordings were made using a single Panasonic M2 video camera 5 m from the sideline, 10 m higher than the field. A Videomedia (Panasonic) VLC 32 editing table made slow motion and frame-by-frame analyses possible. A Wacom Digitizer SD-421-E digital board (Wacom Co., Ltd, Saitama, Japan) and a marking pen, with specially designed software (Arntzen Engineering, Trondheim, Norway) for PC was used to follow movements and to determine distances covered during the game. The following parameters were measured from the video recordings:

Distance covered by a player.
Number of passes, defined as a trial to reach a team player with the ball.
Number of involvements with the ball, defined as all situations where the player is in physical contact with the ball or in direct pressure on an opponent in possession of the ball.
Number of sprints, sprinting for at least 2 s.

Similar parameters for soccer performance have been used in earlier studies (4,25). Before the match analyses were carried out, a thorough reliability testing of the methods for video analyses was performed. The coefficient of reliability was 0.922 for the number of sprints, 0.970 for the number of involvements with the ball, 0.998 for passes, and 0.898 for distance covered during the match (unpublished results).

Statistical analysis. All the results are reported as means ± standard deviation (SD). An ANOVA analysis for repeated measurement was used to determine differences among tests and between groups. Changes from pre- to posttraining in $\dot{V}O_{2max}$, LT, or C_R given in percent is calculated on the basis of the unit $mL \cdot kg^{-0.75} \cdot min^{-1}$. Results were accepted as significant at $P < 0.05$. Group size and statistical power were estimated using nQuery Advisor software (Version 3.0, Statistical Solutions Ltd., Cork, Ireland).

RESULTS

During the training period, three subjects in the TG dropped out because of illness and injuries not related to the training protocol. During the soccer matches, it was not possible to take heart frequency measurements from two subjects in the CG, and three subjects in the CG were unable to play in the soccer matches. There were no differences between the groups in terms of $\dot{V}O_{2max}$ before training, although the TG showed an increase in $\dot{V}O_{2max}$ of 10.8% ($P < 0.05$) after the training period (Table 2).

In the TG, LT and C_R were improved by 16% ($P < 0.05$) and 6.7% ($P < 0.05$), respectively. LT was not statistically changed expressed as percent $\dot{V}O_{2max}$, but in terms of running speed at LT (ν_{Th}) it increased from 11.1 $km \cdot h^{-1}$ to 13.5

TABLE 2. Results from physiological tests (± SD).

	TG (N = 9)		CG (N = 10)	
	Pretraining	Posttraining	Pretraining	Posttraining
$\dot{V}O_{2max}$				
$L \cdot min^{-1}$	4.25 (1.9)	4.59 (1.4)*	4.06 (0.95)	4.11 (0.99)
$mL \cdot kg^{-1} \cdot min^{-1}$	58.1 (4.5)	64.3 (3.9)*	58.4 (4.3)	59.5 (4.4)
$mL \cdot kg^{-0.75} \cdot min^{-1}$	169.9 (9.6)	188.3 (10.6)*	169.2 (9.7)	170.3 (9.8)
LT				
$L \cdot min^{-1}$	3.5 (0.4)	3.96 (0.3)*	3.5 (0.4)	3.46 (0.4)
$mL \cdot kg^{-1} \cdot min^{-1}$	47.8 (5.3)	55.4 (4.1)*	49.5 (3.3)	50.0 (4.1)
$mL \cdot kg^{-0.75} \cdot min^{-1}$	139.9 (15.5)	162.3 (12.2)*	143.7 (15.2)	143.2 (10.9)
% $\dot{V}O_{2max}$	82.4 (3.1)	86.3 (2.1)	86.2 (3.7)	84.2 (2.8)
% f_{cmax}	87.4 (2.3)	87.6 (2.4)	89.2 (3.1)	88.7 (4.2)
ν_{LT} ($km \cdot h^{-1}$)	11.1 (0.7)	13.5 (0.4)*	11.7 (0.4)	11.5 (0.2)
Running economy				
$mL \cdot kg^{-0.75} \cdot m^{-1}$	0.75 (0.05)	0.70 (0.04)*	0.75 (0.04)	0.74 (0.04)
f_{cmax} ($beats \cdot min^{-1}$)	202 (5.5)	203 (5.7)	202 (6.3)	202 (6.3)
$[la^-]_b$ ($mmol \cdot L^{-1}$)	8.1 (1.5)	8.5 (1.9)	7.8 (1.4)	7.9 (1.5)
R	1.17 (0.1)	1.18 (0.1)	1.18 (0.1)	1.18 (0.1)

ν_{LT}, running velocity at LT (3° inclination); $[la^-]_b$ ($mmol \cdot L^{-1}$), blood lactate concentration after $\dot{V}O_{2max}$ testing; R, respiratory exchange ratio.
* $P < 0.05$.

$km \cdot h^{-1}$ ($P < 0.05$). C_R was constant within the range 60–95% $\dot{V}O_{2max}$.

Results from video analyses during games are given in Table 3. The TG increased the distance covered during a game by 20% ($P < 0.01$). The average increase in the number of sprints per player during a match for the TG was 100% ($P < 0.001$), and the number of involvements with the ball increased by 24.1% ($P < 0.05$). The number of passes and the distribution between successful and not successful passes did not change.

Table 4 reflects the work intensity reported as average heart rate in percent of f_{cmax}, during the first and the second halves, as well as during the whole game. From before to after training the TG increased the average percent of f_{cmax} in the game during the second half and during the whole game ($P < 0.05$) (Table 4).

Figure 1 shows the time spent in the different intensity zones (see Methods) in the first and second halves, before and after training. Figure 1 also shows time spent at different intensities during the game after training. The TG had a significantly smaller decline in average percent of f_{cmax} in the second half, at posttraining ($P < 0.05$), and spent 19 min longer in the high-intensity zone (> 90% of f_{cmax}) compared with the CG at the posttraining game ($P < 0.05$). No changes were found in either group in the tests involving speed, strength, jumping height, kicking velocity, and technical test (passing precision) (Table 5).

DISCUSSION

The protocol used to improve the aerobic endurance in this study increased $\dot{V}O_{2max}$ by 10.8% in the TG. No significant changes took place in the CG after the same period of time. This improvement in $\dot{V}O_{2max}$ from endurance training was in accordance with previous studies (21). Given the standard deviation in repeated determination of $\dot{V}O_{2max}$ (3), the number of subjects studied permitted detection of a 4.5% difference between groups (P = 0.05, power = 0.90). The average $\dot{V}O_{2max}$ after training for the TG in the present study is above what is often reported for soccer players. Other studies have shown that the average $\dot{V}O_{2max}$ for international level male soccer players ranges from 55–68 $mL \cdot kg^{-1} \cdot min^{-1}$, with individual values higher than 70 $mL \cdot kg^{-1} \cdot min^{-1}$ (18,24). These values are similar to those found in other team sports, but substantially lower than elite performers in endurance sports, where values close to 90 $mL \cdot kg^{-1} \cdot min^{-1}$ have commonly been found. The fact that no changes occurred in the $\dot{V}O_{2max}$ of the control group is probably because of the lack of high-intensity endurance training during regular soccer practice.

The TG showed an improvement in LT in absolute terms but not relative to $\dot{V}O_{2max}$. In studies using the present LT procedure, well-trained long-distance runners have LT at about 85% $\dot{V}O_{2max}$ (9,10). This is in line with the present results for soccer players. Another LT protocol derived from fixed blood lactate values (e.g., 2 or 4 $mmol \cdot L^{-1}$) would

TABLE 3. Video analyses from soccer matches at pretest and posttest, as average numbers per player and match (± SD).

	TG (N = 9)		CG (N = 10)	
	Pretraining	Posttraining	Pretraining	Posttraining
No. of sprints	6.2 (2.2)	12.4 (4.3)**	6.4 (2.4)	7.5 (2.7)
No. of involvements with ball	47.4 (5.5)	58.8 (6.9)*	50.1 (6.1)	52.4 (6.7)
No. of passes	28.5 (3.5)	30.7 (3.9)	24.8 (3.1)	26.9 (3.9)
Successful passes	19.4 (2.1)	23.5 (2.7)	16.6 (2.0)	18.7 (2.3)
Unsuccessful passes	9.1 (1.9)	7.2 (1.4)	8.2 (1.7)	8.2 (1.8)
Distance covered (m)	8619 (1237)	10,335 (1608)**	9076 (1512)	9137 (1565)

* $P < 0.05$; ** $P < 0.01$.

TABLE 4. Average heart frequency during match (% f_{cmax}) (± SD).

	First Half	Second Half	Total
Pretraining			
CG (N = 8)	83.0 (3.0)	80.0 (2.0)	81.7 (3.3)
TG (N = 9)	84.0 (4.0)	81.2 (2.1)	82.7 (3.4)
Posttraining			
CG (N = 8)	84.2 (3.0)	81.1 (4.2)	82.6 (4.1)
TG (N = 9)	86.3 (3.2)	85.0 (3.0)*	85.6 (3.1)*

* $P < 0.05$.

give the same change in scores from before to after training, which was the focus of this study. The training protocol used in this study was not specifically designed to improve LT. Such a training regimen would normally imply the utilization of work intensity of between 85 and 90% of f_{cmax} (17). Improvements in $\dot{V}O_{2max}$ are, however, normally followed by improved LT. The improvement in LT is therefore a result of the change in $\dot{V}O_{2max}$ and C_R. The TG spent 19 min more than the CG in the high-intensity zone (> 90% of f_{cmax}). This is probably because of increased $\dot{V}O_{2max}$ in the TG, since the fractional utilization of $\dot{V}O_{2max}$ has been shown to be partly dependent on the state of training (9). The ability to perform for longer periods of time at the same relative exercise intensity is, however, more a function of efficiency in usage of glycogen. Thus, the amount of glycogen and the training status of the muscles involved in the exercise are decisive for the maintenance of a specific relative work intensity. Endurance training in soccer, more than a training regimen aimed to improve LT only, should thus emphasize improvement in $\dot{V}O_{2max}$ and, in turn, improve LT.

C_R was also improved by 6.7% in the TG as a result of the training protocol. Improved C_R would, however, be expected on the basis of their more extensive running during practice compared with the CG. More running practice has been shown to affect C_R (9). A question remains, however, whether or not the "soccer specific" work economy of the players was improved. This means the oxygen cost of carrying and trapping the ball, and starting, stopping, and changing direction. This was not addressed in this study. C_R in the present study was higher than that reported earlier (9,10). The reason for this is probably that these studies have used horizontal or 1° inclination treadmill during running, whereas the present study was carried out on 3° inclination. This gives higher $\dot{V}O_2$ at the same speed resulting in higher C_R (lower economy). The C_R was constant within the running velocities just below and higher than LT, and this is consistent with data obtained by Di Prampero et al. (7) and Helgerud (9).

In this study, the work intensity during soccer matches was studied through an analysis of f_c during matches. At pretraining, there were no differences between the TG and the CG. However, the TG improved their average intensity at posttraining. In practical terms, as the results presented in Table 3 show, this means that a player from the CG, having a f_{cmax} of 200 beats·min^{-1}, at posttraining would have an average f_c of 165 beats·min^{-1}, whereas a player from the TG, with the same f_{cmax}, would have an average intensity of 171 beats·min^{-1}. The time spent in the different intensity zones in this experiment correspond with the findings from Rhode and Espersen (19). Improved work intensity as a result of the intervention seems logical, as the average distance covered during a game for the TG increased by 1716 m and the average number of sprints per player increased from 6 to 12. These results support the findings from Smaros (20) showing that the players with the highest $\dot{V}O_{2max}$ had the highest

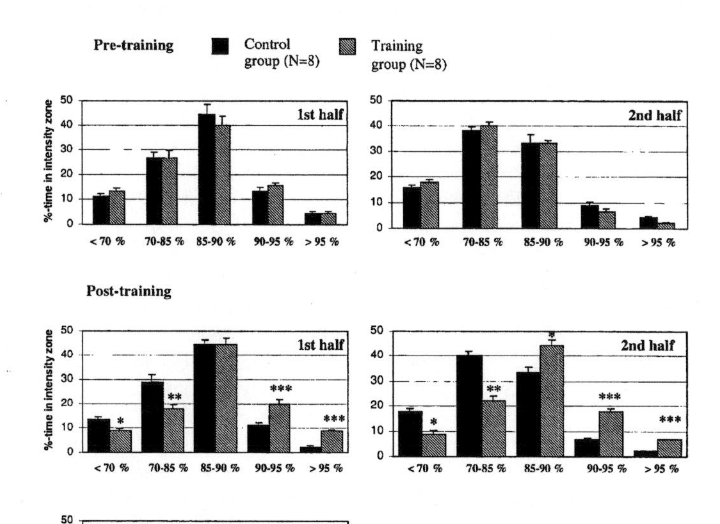

FIGURE 1—*Upper panels* show time spent in the different intensity zones in first and second halves before training. Intensities are expressed in relation to maximal heart rate. *Middle panels* show the corresponding values after training. *Lower panel* shows time spent at different intensities during the game after training. Values are mean ± SD. Significantly different from training group, *P < 0.05; **P < 0.01; ***P < 0.001.

TABLE 5. Results from the strength, speed, jump, and technical tests (± SD).

	TG (N = 9)		CG (N = 10)	
	Pretraining	Posttraining	Pretraining	Posttraining
Running velocity (s)				
10 m	1.88 (0.06)	1.87 (0.05)	1.89 (0.06)	1.89 (0.06)
40 m	5.58 (0.16)	5.56 (0.15)	5.61 (0.18)	5.62 (0.19)
Strength (kg)				
1RM bench press	60.3 (12.7)	59.8 (11.5)	55.8 (10.6)	55.5 (10.4)
1RM 90° squat	146.1 (26.4)	141.9 (25.8)	137.3 (25.1)	129.1 (23.3)
Vertical jump (cm)	54.9 (4.7)	54.7 (3.8)	52.0 (3.7)	52.4 (4.1)
Kicking				
Velocity (km·h^{-1})	106.0 (4.9)	108.0 (6.1)	98.5 (11.5)	99.0 (12.6)
Technique (points):				
First trial	17.4 (5.3)	19.0 (6.9)	18.5 (6.7)	16.2 (4.6)
After $\dot{V}O_{2max}$ test	18.8 (6.1)	16.3 (4.1)	16.2 (5.7)	14.5 (3.8)

number of sprints and took part in more decisive situations during a match than those with a lower $\dot{V}O_{2max}$. The results in the present study also agree with those of Bangsbo et al. (4), who found that the average number of sprints in matches completed by Danish elite players was 19, an activity that covered less than 1 min of the entire game.

Distance covered during a match differed a lot in the measures performed in the early 1970s (14). Recently, however, measurements have become more reliable, and top-level differences are now considered to be quite small. Recent studies showing the distances covered by male players are 10,245 m (23), 9,845 m (16), 10,800 m for Danish elite players (4), and 11,527 m for Australian elite players (25).

The results in the present study showed that an improved $\dot{V}O_{2max}$ gives an enhanced potential to cover a longer running distance at a higher intensity. The distances covered by the subjects correspond with several other studies (16,23). After the training protocol, the TG covered 10,335 m in 61.30 min of effective playing time. Although the TG covered on average 1716 m more at posttraining than at the pretraining match, it is important to note how these improvements are mirrored into soccer performance. An increase of 24% in number of involvements with the ball in the TG, whereas no changes were observed in the CG, shows that a player with higher $\dot{V}O_{2max}$ is able to be involved in more situations, increasing his/her possibility to influence the end result of a match. The TG had 47.4 and 58.8 involvements with the ball throughout a match at pretraining and posttraining, respectively. This is in line with the findings from Withers et al. (25), who showed that Australian elite soccer players on average were involved with the ball 50 times per match.

No differences were found for the quality of passes during a match in the two groups after the training period. However, the average work intensity during a match increased in the TG at posttraining, and still they were able to keep up the quality of passes. Motor skill training at a high intensity level might be the type of training that can alter the percentage of successful passes. The increased number of involvements during the match, however, was not followed by an improved number of passes. The reason seems to be that the evaluation of passes is much more related to technical skill than the evaluation of involvements. The number of passes in the present study was on average 30 per player and match after training, in line with earlier findings (15).

No changes were observed in one-repetition maximum (1RM) squat strength or bench press strength, in vertical jumping height, or in running velocity for any of the groups as expected from the endurance training protocol. On the other hand, one might still expect that regular soccer training should improve some of these skills. In accordance with earlier studies (11,13), the results in the present study also show that aerobic training does not have a negative impact on the strength, speed, and jumping ability. In addition, maximal kicking velocity was not altered by the training protocol, in agreement with previous research showing that improved rate of force development or improved coordination seems to be the trigger mechanism behind velocity development (1,12).

Furthermore, in the present study no changes occurred in the technical kicking, either between groups or between testing conditions, even though lactate values averaged 8.1 mmol·L^{-1} in each group after the $\dot{V}O_{2max}$ determination. However, the technical kicking test used in the present study was not familiar to the players and might have created some initial anxiety, which still would not explain lack of differences after training. Another explanation might be that the technical test used in the present study was too easy for the subjects and thus no differentiation was forthcoming between subjects with or without high levels of blood lactate.

Ideally, endurance training for soccer players should be carried out using the ball. The players might then additionally develop technical and tactical skills similar to situations experienced during the game. Player motivation is also normally considered to be higher when the ball is used. However, the work intensity often is reduced when more technical and tactical elements are involved. Bangsbo et al. (4) showed that playing four against four on a field half the size of a regular soccer field requires higher work intensity than when the field size is reduced to one third of a regular soccer field. If the goal is to train at an intensity zone between 90 and 95% of f_{cmax}, this is difficult to organize in a match situation, especially for teams in lower divisions. Heart rate monitoring systems and a training regimen, where the intensity is relatively easily regulated, are probably necessary to expect similar developments as in this experiment.

CONCLUSION

In the present study, enhancing maximal oxygen uptake led to improved soccer performance, substantiated as distance covered, level of work intensity, number of sprints, and number of involvements with the ball during a match. The increased aerobic endurance had no negative influence on maximal jumping height, strength, speed, kicking velocity, or kicking precision.

The authors are indebted to Robyn Jones, Ph.D., and Fabio Esposito, M.D., for help with the preparation of the manuscript; and to engineer Oddvar Arntzen for the program used to measure the distance covered during a match.

Address for correspondence: Jan Helgerud, Ph.D., Department of Sport Sciences, Norwegian University of Science and Technology, N-7491 Trondheim, Norway; E-mail: jan.helgerud@svt.ntnu.no.

REFERENCES

1. ALMÅSBAKK, B., and J. HOFF. Coordination, the determinant of velocity specificity? *J. Appl. Physiol.* 80:2046–2052, 1996.
2. APOR, P. Successful formulae for fitness training. In: *Science and Football*, T. Reilly, A. Lees, K. Davids, and W. J. Murphy (Eds.). London: E & F.N. Spon, 1988, pp. 95–107.
3. ÅSTRAND, P. O., and K. RODAHL. *Textbook of Work Physiology*, 3rd Ed. New York: McGraw-Hill, 1986, p. 303.
4. BANGSBO, J., L. NØRREGAARD, and F. THORSØE. Activity profile of competition soccer. *Can. J. Sports Sci.* 16:110–116, 1991.
5. BERGH, U., B. SJØDIN, A. FORSBERG, and J. SVEDENHAG. The relationship between body mass and oxygen uptake during running in humans. *Med. Sci. Sports Exerc.* 23:205–211, 1991.
6. COSTILL, D. L., H. THOMASON, and E. ROBERTS. Fractional utilization of the aerobic capacity during distance running. *Med. Sci. Sports Exerc.* 5:248–252, 1973.
7. DI PRAMPERO, P. E., G. ATCHOU, J. C. BRÜCKNER, and C. MOIA. The energetics of endurance running. *Eur. J. Appl. Physiol.* 55:259–266, 1986.
8. DOUGLAS, T. Physiological characteristics of elite soccer players. *Sports Med.* 16:80–96, 1993.
9. HELGERUD, J. Maximal oxygen uptake, anaerobic threshold and running performance in women and men with similar performances levels in marathons. *Eur. J. Appl. Physiol.* 68:155–161, 1994.
10. HELGERUD, J., F. INGJER, and S. B. STRØMME. Sex differences in performance-matched marathon runners. *Eur. J. Appl. Physiol.* 61:433–439, 1990.
11. HENNESSY, L. C., and A. W. S. WATSON. The interference effects of training for strength and endurance simultaneously. *J. Strength Cond. Res.* 8:12–19, 1994.
12. HOFF, J., and B. ALMÅSBAKK. The effects of maximum strength training on throwing velocity and muscle strength in female team handball players. *J. Strength Cond. Res.* 9:255–258, 1995.
13. HOFF, J., J. HELGERUD, and U. WISLØFF. Maximal strength training improves work economy in trained female cross-country skiers. *Med. Sci. Sports Exerc.* 6:870–877, 1999.
14. KNOWLES, J. E., and J. D. BROOKE. A movement analysis of player behavior in soccer match performance. In: *Proceedings of the 8th Conference of the British Society of Sports Psychology, Salford, England, 1974.* London: British Society of Sport Psychology, 1974, pp. 246–256.
15. LUHTANEN, P. Relationships of individual skills, tactical understanding and team skills in Finish junior soccer players. In: *Scientific Olympic Congress Proceedings. Seoul, 1988*, Vol. 2, pp. 1217–1221.
16. OHASHI, J., H. TOGARI, M. ISOKAWA, and S. SUZUKI. Measuring movement speeds and distances covered during soccer match-play. In: *Science and Football*, T. Reilly, A. Lees, K. Davids, and W. J. Murphy (Eds.). London: E. & F.N. Spon, 1988, pp. 329–333.
17. PATE, R. R., and A. KRISKA. Physiological basis of the sex difference in cardiorespiratory endurance. *Sports Med.* 1:87–98, 1984.
18. REILLY, T. Physiological aspects of soccer. *Biol. Sport* 11:3–20, 1994.
19. ROHDE, H. C., and T. ESPERSEN. Work intensity during soccer training and match play. In: *Science and Football*, T. Reilly, A. Lees, K. Davies, and W. J. Murphy (Eds.). London: E. & F.N. Spon, 1988, pp. 68–75.
20. SMAROS, G. Energy usage during a football match. In: *Proceedings of the 1st International Congress on Sports Medicine Applied to Football, Rome, 1980,* L. Vecchiet (Ed.). Rome: D. Guanillo, 1980, pp. 795–801.
21. TABATA, I., K. NISHIMURA, M. KOUZAKI, et al. Effects of moderate-intensity endurance and high-intensity intermittent training on anaerobic capacity and VO_{2max}. *Med. Sci. Sports Exerc.* 28:1327–1330, 1996.
22. THOMAS, V., and T. REILLY. Application of motion analysis to assess performance in competitive football. *Ergonomics* 19:530, 1976. Abstract.
23. VAN GOOL, D., D. VAN GERVEN, and J. BOUTMANS. The physiological load imposed on soccer players during real match-play. In: *Science and Football*, T. Reilly, A. Lees, K. Davids, and W. J. Murphy (Eds.). London: E. & F.N. Spon, 1980, pp. 51–59.
24. WISLØFF, U., J. HELGERUD, and J. HOFF. Strength and endurance of elite soccer players. *Med. Sci. Sports Exerc.* 3:462–467, 1998.
25. WITHERS, R. T., Z. MARICIC, S. WASILEWSKI, and L. KELLY. Match analysis of Australian professional soccer players. *J. Hum. Mov. Stud.* 8:159–176, 1982.

MAXIMAL STRENGTH TRAINING ENHANCES RUNNING ECONOMY AND AEROBIC ENDURANCE PERFORMANCE.

JAN HOFF and JAN HELGERUD

Norwegian University of Science and Technology, Department of Physiology and Biomedical Engineering, N-7489 Trondheim, Norway

ABSTRACT

Purpose: The major purpose of the present study was to determine whether maximal strength squat training using high loads, few repetitions and maximal mobilization of force might improve running economy, and thus an aerobic endurance performance, as has been shown with work economy in previous research. **Methods:** 24 trained subjects from three soccer teams with a mean $\dot{V}O_{2max}$ of 4.36 L, 59.8 mL · kg^{-1} · min^{-1} or 174.5 mL · kg$^{-0.75}$ · min^{-1} participated in the study. The training group (TG) performed maximal strength training, 5 repetitions in 4 series of higher loads than 85% of 1 RM with emphasis on maximal mobilization of force in the concentric action, three times per week for 8 weeks. The control group (CG) trained soccer technical training during the same amount of time. **Results:** 1RM increased with 33.7% from 161.3 kg to 215.6 kg in half squats for the TG with no change in bodyweight, whereas no change was reported for the control group. Rate of force development at a maximal voluntary contraction improved by 52.3% and peak force improved by 9.6% in TG, while no change was observed in the CG. Running economy improved by 4.7% from 0.788 to 0.751 mL · kg$^{-0.75}$ · m^{-1} while no change was observed in the CG. No change was observed in the parameters $\dot{V}O_{2max}$ and Th_{an}. **Conclusion:** Maximal strength training with emphasis on mobilization of force in the concentric action improves 1RM and rate of force development mainly from neural adaptations altering recruitment patterns and result in improved running economy.

Key words: MAXIMAL STRENGTH, RUNNING ECONOMY, NEURAL ADAPTATIONS, RATE OF FORCE DEVELOPMENT, BODY WEIGHT.

Introduction

Pate and Kriska (1984) have described a model that incorporates the three major factors that account for interindividual variance in aerobic endurance performance, namely maximal oxygen uptake (VO_{2max}), anaerobic threshold (Th_{an}) and work economy (C). Numerous published studies support this model (Pollock 1977; Farrell et al 1979; Conley and Krahenbuhl 1980; DiPrampero et al 1986; Bunc and Heller 1989, Bassett and Howley 2000). Thus, the model should serve as a useful framework for the comprehensive study examining the effects of strength training on aerobic endurance performance.

Maximal strength training effects on endurance performance in cross-country double poling has been shown as a result of significant changes in work economy (C), and highly correlated to rate of force development, while no changes are observed in the parameters VO_{2peak} and Th_{an} (Hoff et al 1999).

Johnson et al (1997) also concludes that strength training improves work economy. The results are questioned though, as the strength training intervention in this experiment leads to higher bodyweight, probably through hypertrophy, and that running economy (C_R) thus are overestimated based on principles of allometric scaling (Bergh et al, 1991;Wisløff et al 1999). Also Paavolainen et al (1999), shows improvements in running economy (C_R), but the training intervention is complex, and the total training regime also alters VO_{2max} and to some extent body weight, and the results are thus not easily interpreted.

The maximal strength training effects on work economy showed in highly trained skiers when performing upper body double poling are interesting, but does not necessarily transfer to leg training and running economy. Training adaptations are normally related to training state. An improvement of 29% in work economy for female cross-country skiers when double poling has been shown (Hoff et al 1999), while the better trained male skiers have shown an improvement of 23% and 9% using the same training regime (Hoff et al 2001). Legs have a higher training state than upper body in most people. The fact that upper body work normally only utilizes up to 90% of VO_{2max} in trained skiers, while leg work utilizes 100% of VO_{2max}, due to muscle volume involved, might also have an impact on training effects. The purpose of this study is to determine the effects of maximal strength training with emphasis on maximal mobilization of force on the aerobic performance elements VO_{2max}, Th_{an}, and C_R while running. This training is supposed to primarily alter rate of force development and not induce hypertrophy, and thus not alter body weight. The hypothesis is that C_R at aerobic velocity will improve from leg strength training similar to what have been shown for upper body in previous research, but that the training effects might be smaller.

METHODS

Subjects. Players from male Norwegian soccer teams in 2nd division and the highest junior division participated in the study. Players from each team were randomly placed into either a training group (TG) n=12 or a control group (CG) n=12. Each subject reviewed and signed consent forms approved by the Human Research Review Committee prior to participating in the study. The participating subjects were given information regarding the physical and physiological tests, but were unaware of the hypothesis to be tested. The physical and physiological characteristics of the subjects are presented in Table 1.

TABLE 1. Physical and physiological characteristics of subjects.

	N	Age (yr)	Height (cm)	Mass (kg)	[Hb] ($g \cdot dL^{-1}$)	Hct (%)	VC (L)	FEV_1 (%)
TG	8	23.1	182.0	76.8	14.3	43.8	5.02	89.16
(SD)		(2.7)	(6.0)	(5.5)	(1.0)	(2.0)	(0.81)	(5.06)
CG	10	19.8	181.1	73.3	14.2	43.6	5.27	90.67
(SD)		(1.3)	(5.1)	(6.7)	(1.1)	(1.3)	(0.85)	(4.27)

Mean, Standard Deviations in brackets; [Hb]= Hemoglobin; Hct= Hematocrit; VC= Vital Capacity; FEV_1 =Forced Expiratory Volume.

Apparatus. For [Hb] and Hct determination, blood was drawn from a fingertip and analyzed immediately using the Refletron (Boehringer Manheim, Germany) and Ames microspin (Bayer Diagnostic, Germany) devices, respectively. Vital capacity (VC) and forced expiratory volume in one second (FEV_1) were determined using a flow screen (Jaeger, Germany). Vertical jump height for squat jump (SJ) and counter movement jump(CMJ) and maximal voluntary isometric test was determined using a force platform in combination with software developed specifically for the platform (Bioware, Kistler, Switzerland). Strength training and testing was performed using a competition standard Olympic style bar and weights (T-100G, Eleiko, Sweden).

Time for 10 and 40m sprint test was measured using photocells (Brower Timing, USA) at the start, at 10 meters and at 40 meters. Heart frequency (f_c) was measured by short-range radio telemetry (Polar Sporttester, Polar Electro, Finland). $\dot{V}O_2$, maximal minute ventilation (V_E), respiratory exchange ratio (R) and breathing frequency were measured during each exercise stage using an Ergo Oxyscreen (Jaeger EOS sprint, Germany). Unhemolyzed lactate concentration ($[la^-]_b$), was determined using a YSI Model 1500 Sport Lactate Analyzer (Yellow Springs Instrument Co., USA).

Testing procedures. All of the players within a given team were assessed on the same day, and the tests were performed in the same order. Upon entering the laboratory, hemoglobin concentration [Hb], hematocrit (Hct) and lung function were measured for normative data comparisons. After these preliminary tests, subjects completed a 20-minute warm-up at approximately 50-60 % of VO_{2max}. Vertical jumping tests were then carried out, including Squat jump (SJ), Counter movement jump (CMJ) and a test of maximal voluntary force development against a bar heavier than could be lifted (MVC). The subjects performed three trials in each test. Average of the two best measurements was reported as the test result. Jumping height was determined as the center of mass displacement calculated from force development and measured body mass. The maximum isometric test was determined using a bar and loads so heavy it could not be lifted, placed in a squat rack and fixed at a defined position. Subjects' knee joint angle was 90 degrees in this MVC test, and the position of the bar was similar in both pre- and post-test.

Strength testing consisted of one repetition maximum (1RM) of bench press and of half squats (90□ angle of the knee joints). Peak force was determined from the force curves sampled from the force platform at 500 Hz. Rate of force development (RFD) was determined as the force difference from 10 to 90% of peak force, divided by time used to achieve that difference (ΔF □ Δt^{-1}). A 10 and 40-meter sprint test followed the strength tests. Each subject used 2 trials separated by 5 minutes rest. When ready to sprint, the subjects decided themselves when to start the sprint test from a static position, with the time being recorded when the subjects intercepted the photocell beam.

Following the strength and sprint tests, after a 30-45 minutes break, anaerobic threshold (Th_{an}) and maximal oxygen uptake ($VO_{2\ max}$) were determined during treadmill running at 3□ inclination. The protocol used for measuring Th_{an} and $\dot{V}O_{2\ max}$ has been described previously (Helgerud et al 1990). Briefly, Th_{an} determination began with a 10 minute warm-up at 50-60 % of $\dot{V}O_{2\ max}$, followed by measurement of baseline blood lactate concentration ($[la^-]_b$). Based on previous work (Helgerud et al 1990), the Th_{an} was taken as the power output, $\dot{V}O_2$, or heart rate (f_c) which gave a $\Delta[la^-]_b$ of 1.5 mmol □ L^{-1} above baseline using 5 minute work bouts during a continuous, graded protocol. Subjects performed 5-minute exercise stages progressing in intensity between 60 and 95 % of $VO_{2\ max}$. Running speed was increased by one km · h^{-1} at each stage, after a 20 second pause for blood sampling from a finger tip. After reaching Th_{an}, treadmill speed was increased to a level which brought the subject to $\dot{V}O_{2max}$ and to exhaustion after about 3 minutes. Running economy (C_R) was calculated at Th_{an} , the maximal exercise intensity at which it has been shown that a reliable relationship exist between intensity and oxygen uptake ($\dot{V}O_2$)(Helgerud 1994, Bunc and Heller 1989). The highest f_c during the last minute was taken as maximal heart frequency ($f_{c\ max}$).

Allometric scaling.

Comparisons between athletes of capacities like VO_{2max} and maximal strength (1RM) are often made in terms of absolute measures (L · min^{-1}, kg) or relative to body weight (mL · kg^{-1} · min^{-1}) or (kg · $kgbw^{-1}$) both of which are both very routine and functionally imprecise. The oxygen cost of running at a standard velocity does not increase in direct proportion to body mass in trained individuals, and similarly strength does not increase in direct proportion to body mass. Dimensional scaling suggest that comparisons between a small and a bigger individual should be expressed by kg bodyweight raised to the power of 0.67 as mL · kg^{-1} · min^{-1} or kg · $kgbw^{-1}$ (Åstrand and Rodahl 1986; Bergh et al 1991, Wisløff et al 1998). Based on descriptive data Bergh et al (1991) found that comparisons of VO_{2max} should be expressed relative to body mass raised to the power of 0.75 when running. If dimensional scaling is not used, both relative strength and relative endurance will underestimate the big athlete and overestimate the small one (Wisløff et al 1998). In an intervention study where bodyweight might be altered from the training regime imposed, or for other reasons, allometric scaling is important when expressing gross oxygen cost of activity or work economy. If bodyweight is gained during an experiment, measuring running economy (CR), improvements in work economy will be overestimated expressing oxygen cost per kg body weight and meter (mL · kg^{-1} · m^{-1}). Based on this rationale, when comparisons of work economy are done between individuals or within individuals at different points in time CR should be expressed as mL raised to the power of -0.75.

Exclusion criteria. Subjects were excluded if failing to carry out 70% of the training intervention. Because of the possibilities for internal rivalry, subjects in the control group were excluded if 1RM improved more than 10% during the training period. 4 subjects in TG were excluded while not having performed 70% of the training intervention, because of injuries in soccer training or matches. Two subjects in CG group could not resist training maximal strength and improved their 1RM more than 10% during the experiment and were subsequently excluded from the material. In the analyses, TG consists of 8 subjects and CG of 10 subjects.

Statistical analysis. All of the results are reported as means, and standard deviations (SD) calculated by conventional procedures. ANOVA repeated measurement analysis was used to determine differences between tests and between the groups. Correlations were calculated by means of Pearson's product moment r. Differences at a set point in time were calculated using a T-test. Results were accepted as significant at $P<0.05$.

RESULTS

Running economy, i.e. oxygen cost per meter running improved by 4.7 % in the TG, and showed a significant time x group interaction [$F(1,16) = 14.29$; $P = 0.002$] (Figure 1), while no change occurred in the CG. Independent of body weight, oxygen consumption per meter (L.m-1) for the TG was reduced by 4.95%.

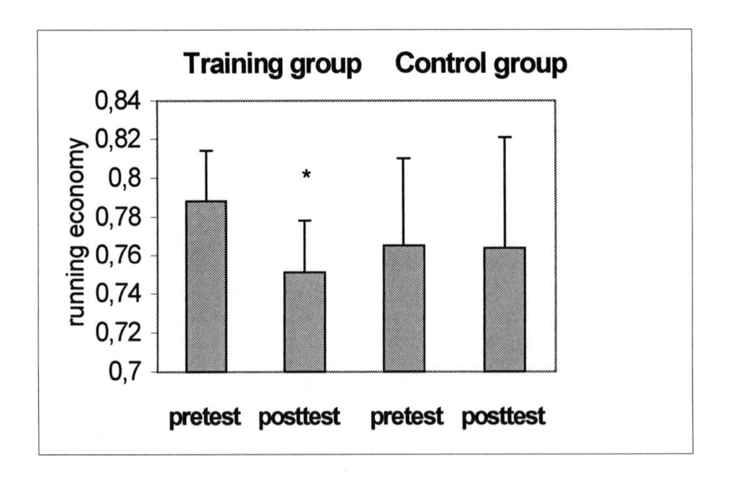

Figure 1. Changes in running economy ($mL \cdot kg^{-0.75} \cdot m^{-1}$) at Th_{an} from pre- to posttest. * = significantly different from pretest ($P<0.05$).

The TG carried out 89 % of the designed strength training regime with high loads and emphasis on maximal mobilization of force. The training regime took 15 minutes to perform each of the three training sessions per week, and represents 45 minutes per week in addition to the 8 hour 30 minutes ordinary soccer training each week. TG significantly [F(1,16) = 66.64; P = 0.000] improved 1RM in half squats by 33.7% (Table 2). There was no difference between the groups before the intervention. Body mass did not change in either of the groups, and consequently relative strength (1RM $m_b^{-0.67}$) showed a similar increase as maximal strength for TG. For the CG, relative strength did not change. Training improved peak force at MVC significantly [F(1,16) = 8.00; P = 0.012] by 9.6% in the TG. Training significantly enhanced RFD by 52.3% [F(1,16) = 5.83; P = 0.028] in the TG.

No group x time interactions was found for jumping height, for CMJ or for SJ.

Significant time x group interaction was found for 10m sprint [F(1,16) = 6.50; P = 0.021] and for 40m sprint [F(1,16) = 8.82; P = 0.009] for the TG, with improvements of 5.2 and 2.3 % respectively.

TABLE 2. Results from strength and force development in squat, jump and sprint tests.

	TG (N=8)		CG (N=10)	
	Pre-training	Post-training	Pre-training	Post-training
Squat:				
1RM (kg)	161.3 (25.3)	215.6 (22.4)*	162.9 (17.4)	159.2 (15.1)
1RM ($kg \cdot m_b^{-0.67}$)	8.79 (1.35)	11.79 (1.23)*	9.17 (1.00)	8.56 (0.86)
MVC:				
Peak force (N)	1835 (690)	2011 (753)*	2068 (364)	2029 (342)
RFD ($N \cdot s^{-1}$)	1662 (843)	2531 (1024)*	1731 (823)	1691 (1012)
Body mass (m_b)(kg)	76.8 (5.5)	76.5 (5.4)	73.3 (6.7)	73.3(7.0)
Jump tests:				
CMJ (cm)	44.1 (3.5)	46.8 (4.4)	45.3 (5.1)	45.3 (6.0)
SJ (cm)	38.6 (2.5)	39.8 (2.4)	38.5 (6.0)	38.8 (4.2)
Sprint:				
10m	1.91 (0.07)	1.81 (0.09)*	1.84 (0.07)	1.82 (0.04)
40m	5.68 (0.21)	5.55 (0.16)*	5.55 (0.16)	5.52 (0.18)

Mean, Standard Deviation in brackets; 1RM= One Repetition Maximum; MVC= Maximal Voluntary Contraction; RFD= Rate of Force Development; CMJ= Counter Movement Jump; SJ= Squat Jump; * , $p<0.05$.

For the $\dot{V}O_{2max}$ results, no time x group interactions were found neither by expressing oxygen consumption in liters per minute or divided by bodyweight, nor by using allometric scaling (Table 3). Anaerobic threshold Th_{an} showed no time x group interactions independent of expression used.

Lactate concentration, respiratory exchange ratio and f_{cmax} did not change as a result of the training protocol.

TABLE 3. Results from physiological aerobic endurance tests.

	TG (N=8)		CG (N=10)	
	Pre-training	Post-training	Pre-training	Post-training
VO_{2max}				
$L \cdot min^{-1}$	4.63 (0.51)	4.60 (0.46)	4.32 (0.92)	4.36 (0.95)
$ml \cdot kg^{-1} \cdot min^{-1}$	60.3 (3.3)	60.2 (3.7)	59.0 (4.5)	59.6 (4.4)
$ml \cdot kg^{-0.75} \cdot min^{-1}$	178.6 (13.3)	178.0 (13.4)	172.5 (15.4)	174.4 (16.3)
Th_{an}				
$L \cdot min^{-1}$	3.96 (0.34)	3.95 (0.37)	3.61 (0.33)	3.69 (0.35)
$ml \cdot kg^{-1} \cdot min^{-1}$	51.8 (4.4)	51.6 (4.9)	49.3 (4.7)	50.3 (5.0)
$ml \cdot kg^{-0.75} \cdot min^{-1}$	152.7 (13.1)	152.7 (14.3)	144.1 (13.6)	147.3 (14.4)
% VO_{2max}	85.5 (3.0)	85.8 (2.4)	83.6 (3.7)	84.6 (3.1)
% f_{cmax}	88.0 (3.6)	88.1 (2.9)	88.5 (3.3)	88.9 (3.3)
v_{Th}, $km \cdot h^{-1}$	11.6 (0.5)	12.2 (0.8)	11.3 (0.7)	11.5 (0.9)
Running economy				
$mL \cdot kg^{-0.75} \cdot m^{-1}$	0.788 (0.026)	0.751 (0.027)*	0.765 (0.045)	0.764 (0.057)
f_{cmax} ($beats \cdot min^{-1}$)	202.4 (4.1)	203.1 (4.7)	203.1 (6.4)	203.8 (6.3)
$[la^-]_b$ ($mmol \cdot L^{-1}$)	8.1 (2.6)	6.7 (0.8)	7.7 (1.7)	7.8 (1.3)
R	1.10 (0.1)	1.11 (0.1)	1.16 (0.1)	1.15 (0.1)

Mean, Standard Deviation in brackets; v_{Th} = running velocity at Th_{an} (3° inclination); $[la^-]_b$ ($mmol \cdot L^{-1}$)= blood lactate concentration after VO_{2max} testing; R= highest respiratory exchange ratio during VO_{2max} testing; * , $p<0.05$.

Running economy is improved at all measured velocities (Fig. 2). Both at pretest and at posttest, running economy is significantly different between velocities that are 2 $km \cdot h^{-1}$ apart.

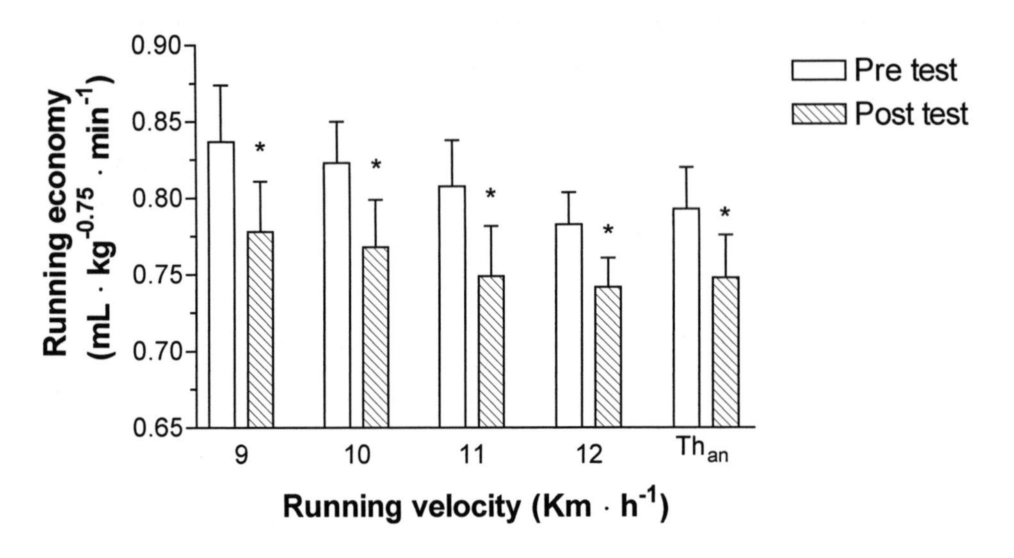

Figure 2. Running economy at different treadmill velocities at 3 degrees inclination.

Discussion

The main hypothesis in this experiment, that running economy is improved from the training regime involving few repetitions, high loads and maximal mobilization of force in squat training is met by the significant 4.7% improvement. This is in line with the findings from upper body work (Hoff et al 1999), and in line with the indications made by Hickson (1988), Johnston et al (1997) and Paavolainen et al (1999), but contrary to Bishop et al (1999). No change was observed in the other elements in the Pate and Kriska (1984) model, declaring aerobic performance, namely VO_{2max} and Th_{an}.

Running economy, or gross oxygen uptake at a standard sub-maximal work rate is taken as a reflection of work efficiency. Intra-individual variations in gross oxygen cost of running at a standard submaximal velocity has been shown by Costill et al (1973) and Conley and Krahenbuhl (1980), among others. The cause of this variability is complex, and anatomical traits, mechanical skill, neuromuscular skill and storage of elastic energy are important (Pate and Kriska 1984). Several experiments report similar values for C_R between male and female distance runners (Daniels et al 1986; Padilla et al 1992), even though with of hips, length of bones and stride, and greater fat deposition on the hips and thighs has been mentioned as possible mechanical disadvantages for female runners (Daniels et al 1977; Pate and Kriska 1984). Several possible mechanisms behind an improved C_R are proposed. As 1RM increases, the percentage of maximal strength that is taxed at a submaximal workload is markedly lower, and might explain why the muscles work efficiency improves (Hoff et al 1999). With increased maximal strength and increased rate of force development, an increase in power production and a shift in the power-load curve is shown, and may contribute to a relatively lower taxation of power production, and thus an improved work efficiency (Hoff et al 2001). Dalleau et al (1998) have shown that the energy cost of running is significantly related to the stiffness of the propulsive leg, which might indicate that increased stiffness, or improved muscular regulation of stiffness could improve C_R. Also a circulatory explanation have been used (Hoff et al 1999).

After 8 weeks of maximal strength training with emphasis on mobilization of force in the concentric part of the squat combined with the subjects' customary soccer training, 1RM increased significantly as hypothesized. An increase of 33.7% was however higher than expected from previous studies, but still well within the range of former studies (Almåsbakk & Hoff 1996, Bishop et al 1999, Hoff & Almåsbakk 1996). Normally one expects a lower trainability the higher the level of fitness. The subjects in this study showed similar leg strength as elite soccer players before the experiment (Wisløff et al. 1998), but compared to strength trained athletes the absolute strength is not very high. The enhanced 1RM did not alter the subjects' bodyweight, as was also hypothesized and in line with previous findings (Hoff et al 2000, Almåsbakk & Hoff 1996, Hoff & Almåsbakk 1995), indicating that the training response is from neural adaptations rather than from hypertrophy (Behm 1995). The training regime imposed on the subjects was little time consuming, and represents only approximately 15 minutes per training session, or 45 minutes per week, as it was carried out directly at the end of a normal soccer training session and there was no need for an extra warm-up period. Relative strength increased in the same amount as absolute strength, as bodyweight did not change. As strength does not increase proportional to body weight allometric scaling is used to establish relative strength values comparable between big and smaller subjects as theorized by Åstrand and Rodahl (1986).

In the MVC static strength test RFD was significantly improved by 52.3%. This is in line with findings from this type of training intervention, previously shown for upper body work (Hoff et al 1999). It is interesting though, that the highly trained hip and leg muscles respond in a similar way as the much less used and trained upper body muscles, even if even higher improvements in RFD is found in upper body muscles (Almåsbakk and Hoff 1996). Peak force showed a much lesser improvement of 9.6%, also in line with previous findings

(Hoff et al 1999), indicating that the training response probably is connected to the recruitment pattern rather than the development of maximal force.

The improved 1RM and RFD do not alter jumping height, neither in a counter-movement jump, nor in a squat jump. Sprinting times however, improves significantly both for the 10m sprint and for the 40m sprint. The correlation between strength and performance is higher for the 10m than for the 40m, probably reflecting the higher dependence of acceleration and thus relation to force in the shorter distance. That jumping height does not increase is different from other findings (Hoff et al 2000), but probably reflect the fact that jumping is sparsely reflected in soccer training and matches, but sprints are. Previous research points to the fact that improvements in high velocity movements from enhanced maximal strength are dependent upon the high velocity movement being trained within the same period of time (Hoff & Almåsbakk 1995, Voigt and Clausen 1990).

VO_{2max} for the subjects in this experiment was similar to what has been reported in previous studies (Wisløff et al 1998, Davies et al 1992, Williams et al 1973) at a high level of soccer performance. The level of VO_{2max} characterize the subjects as endurance trained, even if the average VO_{2max} given both in liters and in $mL \cdot kg^{-1} \cdot min^{-1}$ is far from what is reported for endurance athletes. Body mass is however higher than what is normally seen between endurance athletes, reflecting the body contact and physical demanding duels during the game, where muscle strength is needed. Reporting and comparing VO_{2max} as $mL \cdot kg^{-1} \cdot min^{-1}$ between subjects of different body size is not biologically correct, as the aerobic capacity does not increase proportionally to body weight, but rather to body weight raised to the power of 0.67 in trained mammals (Wisløff et al 1998, Günther 1975, Åstrand & Rodahl 1986). Not taking allometric scaling into account when comparing both endurance and strength capacities will underestimate the big athlete, and overestimate the small one in terms of performance capacity. The difference between the middle/long distance runner and the soccer player are thus smaller than the VO_{2max} values reported as $mL \cdot kg^{-1} \cdot min^{-1}$ would indicate. Bergh et al (1991) have showed from descriptive data that for running, values for VO_{2max} should be reported divided by body weight raised to the power of 0.75 to be size independent. Similar findings has been confirmed by others (Wisløff et al 1998) and relative maximal aerobic capacity is thus reported as $mL \cdot kg^{-0.75} \cdot min^{-1}$ in this study. The same theoretical and descriptive basis also serves for reporting running economy as $mL \cdot kg^{-0.75} \cdot m^{-1}$.

Th_{an} are reported within a normal area for soccer players (Bangsbo 1994, Reilly 1990), with an average for both groups close to 85% of VO_{2max} . Even marathon runners, who compete at an intensity close to anaerobic threshold does not have a higher Than in percentage of VO_{2max} (Helgerud et al 1990; Helgerud 1993). Th_{an} at 88% of f_{cmax} in this material, means for the soccer players an average intensity during the game of 179 beats per minute, as Th_{an} is reported to be the average intensity during a game (Bangsbo 1994, Reilly 1990). R values and $[la^-]_b$ values show that maximal aerobic capacity is reached and serve as assisting criteria during the VO_{2max} test. f_{cmax} is within the normal values for this age group. Running economy, or gross oxygen uptake at a standardized velocity was shown to change with running velocity lower than Th_{an} when the difference in velocity was 2 km $\cdot h^{-1}$. This is different from previously reported, where similar values for running economy has been found (Helgerud 1994), or increased oxygen cost has been found at increased velocities (Svedenhag and Sjødin 1994) for trained long distance runners. Soccer players might have a relatively better running technique at higher velocities than long distance runners.

Conclusion

The result of the present study show that running economy might be improved from a maximal strength training regime based upon high loads, few repetitions and emphasis on mobilization of force in the concentric action. No change in maximal oxygen consumption or anaerobic threshold occurred, in line with what has been found for upper body work. The improved strength is shown without altering body weight. The parameter showing the greatest change was rate of force development, indicating that the main training response is from neural adaptations and changes in recruitment patterns.

References

1. Almåsbakk B, Hoff J. Coordination, the determinant of velocity specificity? *J. Appl. Physiol.* 1996:80(5):2046-2052.

2. Bangsbo J, Physiological demands. In: Football (Soccer). B. Ekblom (Ed.). London. Blackwell Scientific Publishing. 1994: 53-59.

3. Bassett DR Jr, Howley ET. Limiting factors for maximum oxygen uptake and determinants of endurance performance. Med Sci Sports Exerc 2000 32(1):70-84

4. Behm,DG. and Sale DG. Intended rather than actual movement velocity determines velocity-specific training response, *J. Appl. Physiol.* 1993:74: 359-368.

5. Bergh U, Sjødin B, Forsberg A, Svedenhag J. The relationship between body mass and oxygen uptake during running in humans. *Med. Sci. Sports Exerc.* 1991:23:205-211.

6. Bishop D, Jenkins DG, Macinnon LT, Mceniery M. and Carey MF. The effects of strength training on endurance performance and muscle characteristics. *Med. Sci. Sports Exerc.* 1999:31(6):886-891.

7. Bunc V. and Heller J. Energy cost of running in similarly trained men and women. *Eur. J. Appl. Physiol.* 1989:59:178-183.

8. Conley DL. and Krahenbuhl GS. Running economy and distance running performance of highly trained athletes. *Med. Sci. Sports Exerc.* 1980:12:248-252.

9. Dalleau G, Belli A, Bourdin M and Lacour J R. The spring-mass model and the energy cost of treadmill running. *Eur. J. Appl. Physiol*. 1998: 77: 257-263.

10. Daniels J, Scardina N, Hayes J and Foley P. Elite and subelite female middle- and long-distance runners. In: Landers DM (ed) Sport and elite performers. Human Kinetics, Champaign. 1986:57-72.

11. Davis J A, Brewer J and Atkin D. Pre-season physiological characteristics of English first and second division soccer players. *J. Sport Sci.* 1992: 10: 541-547.

12. Di Prampero Å E, Capelli C, Pagliaro Å, Antonutta G, Giradis M, Zamparo Å and Soule R G. Energetics of best performances in middle-distance running. *J. Appl. Physiol.* 1993: 74: 2318-2324.

13. DiPrampero PE, Atcho G, Brückner JC. and Moia C. The energetics of endurance running. *Eur. J. Appl. Physiol.* 1986:55:259-266.

14. Helgerud J. Maximal oxygen uptake, anaerobic threshold and running economy in women and men with similar performances level in marathons. *Eur. J. Appl. Physiol.* 1994:68:155-161.

15. Helgerud J, Ingjer F and Strømme S. Sex differences in performance-matched marathon runners. *Eur. J. Appl. Physiol.* 1990: 61: 433-439.

16. Hickson RC, Dvorak BA, Gorostiaga EM, Kurowski TT, Foster C. Potential for strength and endurance training to amplify endurance performance. *J. Appl. Physiol.* 1988:65: 2285-2290.

17. Hoff J, Almåsbakk B. The effects of maximum strength training on throwing velocity and muscle strength in female team-handball players. *J. Strength Cond. Res.* 1995:9(4):255-258.

18. Hoff J, Helgerud J. and Wisløff U. Maximal strength training improves work economy in trained female cross-country skiers. *Med Sci Sports Exerc.* 1999:31(6):870-877.

19. Hoff J, Berdahl G O and Bråten S. In Science and skiing II. Eds: Müller et al. 2000 (in press)

20. Hoff J, Helgerud J and Wisløff U. Endurance training in the next millenium: Muscular strength training effects on aerobic endurance performance. A review. *The American J. Med. Sport* 2001: (in press).

21. Johnston RE, Quinn TJ, Kertzer R. and Vroman NB. Strength training in female distance runners: Impact on running economy. *J Strength Cond Res.* 1997: 11(4):224-229.

22. Padilla S, Bourdin M, Barthélémy, Lacour JR. Physiological correlates of middle distance running performance. A comparative study between men and women. *Eur. J. Appl. Physiol.* 1992:65:561-566.

23. Pate RR, Kriska A. Physiological basis of the sex difference in cardiorespiratory endurance. *Sports Med.*1984:1: 87-98.

24. Paavolainen L, Häkkinen K, Hämäläinen I, Nummela A. and Rusko H. Explosive strength training improve 5-km running time by improving running economy and muscle power. *J. Appl. Physiol.* 1999:86(5):1527-1533.

25. Reilly T. Football. In: Physiology of sports. T.Reilly, N. Secher, P. Snell and C. Williams (Eds.). London. E & F.N. Spon. 1990: 371-425.

26. Shepard R J. General consideration. In: Endurance in sport. R J Shepard and P O Åstrand (Eds.) London. Blackwell Scientific Publications. 1992: 21-35.

27. Svedenhag J and Sjødin B. Body-mass-modified running economy and step length in elite male middle and long distance runners. *Int. J. Sports Med.* 1994:5:255-261.

28. Voigt M and Klausen C. Changes in muscle strength and speed of an unloaded movement after different training programs. *Eur. J. Appl. Physiol.* 1990: 60: 370-376.

29. Wisøff U, Helgerud J. and Hoff J. Strength and endurance of elite soccer players. *Med. Sci. Sports Exerc.* 1998:30(3):462-467.

30. Åstrand P-O, Rodahl K. Textbook of work physiology. McGraw-Hill Book Company, 1986, New York

PRE-SEASON CONCURRENT STRENGTH AND ENDURAN
DEVELOPMENT IN ELITE SOCCER PLAYERS

Jan Helgerud, Ole J. Kemi, Jan Hoff
Department of Physiology and Biomedical Engineering, Norwegian University of Science and Technology, N-7489 Trondheim Norway.

Abstract
The aim of this study was to intervene in an elite soccer team using concurrent high intensity long interval training and maximal strength training. The hypothesis was that the responses from each intervention would be found to a similar degree as if the strength or the endurance intervention took place alone. Twenty-one elite soccer players from Molde FC, Norway, having recently participated in European Champions League took part in the study. During an eight-week intervention VO_{2max} increased from 60.5±4.8 to 65.7±5.2 $mL \cdot kg^{-1} \cdot min^{-1}$, and half squats one repetition maximum increased from 115.7±23.1 to 176.4±18.2 kg. 10m sprint improved by 0.06 sec or close to half a meter. Vertical jumping height increased significantly by 3 cm. There seem to be no negative effects from carrying out concurrent high intensity aerobic training and maximal strength training. Both maximal strength and high intensity long interval training should be included in pre season training for top level soccer players to increase performance level.

Introduction

Strength and endurance share importance when evaluating physical resources and the ability to perform international level soccer matches. Maximal strength is the basic quality that influences the ability to accelerate, following Newton's second law of motion. An increase in maximal strength is usually connected with an increase in relative strength an therefore with improvement of power abilities. A significant relationship has been observed between one repetition maximum (1RM) and acceleration and movement velocity (Bührle &

Schmidtbleicher 1977; Hoff et al. 2001) This maximal strength – power performance relationship is supported by jump test results as well as in 30m sprint results (Schmidtbleicher 1992; Hoff et al. 2001). During the 90 minutes soccer match sprint activities are short both in terms of distance and time, but comprise the most interesting and decisive part of the game. On average a sprint occur every 90 sec of play (Reilly and Thomas 1976) and is no longer than 2-4 sec (Reilly and Thomas 1976; Bangsbo 1991; O'Donoghue 2001). Correspondingly, recent studies have shown that 96% of sprint bouts are shorter than 30m, and 49% being shorter than 10m (Valquer 1998). Sprint bouts are often performed with sudden change of direction and/or from a running start accentuating the accelerative component even more (Withers 1982). During a game a professional soccer player perform on average 50 turns sustaining forceful contractions to maintain balance and control and exert acceleration to keep control of the ball and getting into position (Withers 1982). Sprinting only constitute 1 to 11% of the total match distance (Bangsbo 1991; Reilly and Thomas 1976) corresponding to 0.5 – 3% of the effective play time (Bangsbo 1991, 1992; O'Donoghue 2001; Ali 1991). In terms of sprinting distance 974±246 m (Reilly and Thomas 1976), 666±311m (Withers 1982) and from 231±141m to 557±228m depending on players position, forwards being the players conducting more sprints (Rienzi 2000). On average players carry out 6 to 12 sprints during a match (Helgerud et al. 2001).

During the match a soccer player covers 8 to 12 km distance at an average intensity close to lactate threshold (LT), or 80-90% of maximal heart frequency (Helgerud et al 2001). The high intensity bouts that is dependent on anaerobic or alactatic energy sources are only restored using aerobic energy, and makes it necessary for the player to spend substantial time at an intensity lower than LT. A significant correlation between maximal oxygen uptake (VO_{2max}) and distance covered during a game is shown (Smaros 1980; Thomas & Reilly 1976). An improvement in VO_{2max} with 6 $mL \cdot kg^{-1} \cdot min^{-1}$ showed an improvement in distance covered of 1700m, and led to 100% increase in number of sprints and 25% increase in involvement with the ball (Helgerud et al. 2001).

Several authors have concluded that endurance training inhibits or interferes with strength development (Chromiak and Mulvaney 1990; Dudley and Djamil 1985; Hennessy and Watson 1994; Nelson 1990). However, Helgerud et al. (2001) showed substantial gain in VO_{2max} during an 8 week intervention with no reduction in sprinting or jumping abilities. Similarly maximal strength training intervention resulting in substantial improvements in sprinting times and jumping height as well as running economy showed no reduction in

VO_{2max} or LT (Hoff et al. 2001, 2002). As the physiological responses depends on quite different biological processes it is not logical that strength should inhibit endurance or vice versa as long as sufficient time and quality of restitution is available.

The aim of this study is to intervene in an elite soccer team using concurrent high intensity long interval endurance training and maximal strength training. The hypothesis is that the responses shown from each of the interventions will be found to a similar degree as if one intervention was used. That an improvement in VO_{2max} similar to Helgerud et al. (2001) will be shown from the endurance intervention, and enhanced sprinting times, jumping height and running economy will follow the maximal strength part is hypothesized.

Methods

Subjects

Twenty-one male elite soccer players from Molde FC (Molde, Norway) took part in the study. Molde FC has recently gained international status, successfully competing in the Champions League UEFA tournament. The team are currently placed second in the Norwegian Premier League. The players studied were all full time professional soccer players and trained on a daily basis. The player's physical characteristic is presented in Table 1. Each subject reviewed and signed consent forms approved by the Human Research Review Committee prior to participating in the study.

Table 1. Physical characteristics of players

	Age (yrs)	Height (cm)	Mass (kg)	Maximal heart rate (beats · min^{-1})
(n=21)	**25.0 ±2.9**	**183.9 ± 5.4**	**78.4 ± 7.4**	**198 ± 9**

Testing.

A 20-meter sprint test were performed after 20 minutes of thorough warm-up at approximately 50-60 % of VO_{2max}.. The tests were performed on an indoor handball field with a parquet floor. Time was recorded by photocells (Brower Timing, USA). Each subject carried out 2 trials in each sprint test separated by 5 minutes of rest. When ready to sprint, the subjects decided themselves when to start the sprint test from a static position, with the time being recorded when the subjects intercepted the photocell beam. Vertical jump height was determined using a force platform with a software specifically developed for the platform (Bioware, Kistler, Switzerland). Jumping height was determined as the center of mass displacement calculated from force development and measured body mass. Strength testing consisted of one repetition maximum of half squats (90° angle of the knee joints) performed with a competition standard Olympic style bar and weights (T-100G, Eleiko, Sweden). The players were familiar with half squats as part of their regular strength training programs.

After the sprint and strength tests each player ran for 10 minutes on a motorized treadmill (Challenger LE5000) at 50 - 60 % of VO_{2max} , the treadmill speed was increased to 11 $km \cdot h^{-1}$ and kept there for 5 min. The average value of oxygen uptake (VO_2) between 4.0 and 4.5 min was used to calculate running economy (CR). The speed of the treadmill was then increased every minute to a level that brought the subject close to exhaustion after approximately 5 minutes. Inclination was constant at 3 degrees. Immediately after VO_{2max} determination, each subject ran for 2 minutes at an exercise intensity of 50 - 60 % of VO_{2max} directly followed by a supramaximal intensity run, resulting in exhaustion after ~3 minutes. Heart rate (f_c) was determined using short-range radio telemetry (Polar Accurex Plus, Polar Electro, Finland). The highest heart frequency during the last minute of the supraintensity run was recorded as f_{cmax}. VO_2, minute ventilation (V_E) and breathing frequency (f_b) were measured during work using a Cortex Metamax II (Cortex, Leipzig, Germany). The Cortex metabolic test system has been validated in our laboratory (Torvik and Helgerud 2001). . We routinely test VO_{2max} after the strength test and get similar VO_{2max} as when performing the treadmill test on a separate day (unpublished results). The specific procedure for VO_{2max} and f_{cmax} determination is routinely used and has been previously described (Helgerud 1994).

Training protocol.

The aerobic training intervention after 10 min warm up consisted of interval training, comprising 4 times 4 minutes running at a treadmill (3 degrees inclination) at 90-95 % of f_{cmax} for each player, separated by periods of 3 minutes jogging at 50-60 % of f_{cmax}. After 15 min break the maximal strength training: four-repetition maximum of half squats (90 ° angle of the knee joints), four series with emphasis on maximal mobilization in the concentric phase using a bar and weights, was carried out. 3 min rest between each series was used. The training session lasted one hour. The athletes were familiar with both training interventions as part of their regular training program. This training protocol was administered twice per week over an 8-wk period pre-season. A regular week of training consisted of 6 times 1.5h practice and games with emphasis on technical and tactical aspects of the game, a total of 11 hours effective training per week in the pre-season period.

Allometric scaling.

Comparisons between athletes of capacities like VO_{2max} and maximal strength (1RM) are often made in terms of absolute measures ($L \cdot min^{-1}$, kg) or relative to body weight ($mL \cdot kg^{-1} \cdot min^{-1}$) or ($kg \cdot kgbw^{-1}$) both of which are both very routine and functionally imprecise. The oxygen cost of running at a standard velocity does not increase in direct proportion to body mass in trained individuals, and similarly strength does not increase in direct proportion to body mass. Dimensional scaling suggest that comparisons between a small and a bigger individual should be expressed by kg bodyweight raised to the power of 0.67 as $mL \cdot kg^{-1} \cdot min^{-1}$ or $kg \cdot kgbw^{-1}$ (Åstrand and Rodahl 1986). Based on descriptive data Bergh et al (1991) and Helgerud (1994) found that comparisons of VO_{2max} should be expressed relative to body mass raised to the power of 0.75 when running. If dimensional scaling is not used, both relative strength and relative endurance will underestimate the big athlete and overestimate the small one (Wisløff et al 1998). In an intervention study where bodyweight might be altered from the training regime imposed, or for other reasons, allometric scaling is important when expressing gross oxygen cost of activity or work economy. If bodyweight is gained during an experiment, measuring running economy (CR), improvements in work economy will be overestimated expressing oxygen cost per kg body weight and meter ($mL \cdot kg^{-1} \cdot m^{-1}$). Based on this rationale, when comparisons of work economy are carried out between individuals or within individuals at different points in time, CR should be expressed as $mL \cdot kg^{-0.75} \cdot m^{-1}$.

Statistical analyses

Data are presented as mean ± SD. Student t-test was used to determine changes from pre- to posttest. Pearson' product-moment correlation were used to determine the relations between selected parameters. Allometric equations was used to determine the relationship between VO_{2max} /maximal strength (1RM) and body mass (Wisløff et al 1998). $P < 0.05$ was considered statistically significant. Group size and statistical power were estimated using nQuery Advisor software (Version 3.0, Statistical Solutions Ltd., Cork, Ireland). Given the standard deviation in repeated determination of VO_{2max} (Åstrand and Rodahl 1986), the number of subjects studied permitted detection of a 2.7 % difference between pre- and post training ($p=0.05$, power=0.90).

Results

The VO_{2max} and maximal strength (1RM squats) were improved by 8.1% ($p<0.001$) and 49.2% ($p<0.001$), respectively after the training period (Table 2). Body mass increased significantly 1.0 kg from pre- to post-test. If three goalkeepers are excluded from the material mean VO_{2max} after training was 5.27 (0.54) L· min^{-1} and 66.5 (5.0) mL· kg^{-1} · min^{-1}.

The CR at 11 km · h^{-1} improved by 3.7% from 0.85 (0.03) mL· $kg^{-0.75}$ · m^{-1} pre-testing to 0.82 (0.03) mL· $kg^{-0.75}$ · m^{-1} post-testing. Average heart rate decreased from 178 (8) to 170 (8)($p<0.001$), average respiratory exchange ratio (R) decreased from 1.02 (0.05) to 0.97(0.05) and minute ventilation (V_E) decreased from 109.4 (15.4) to 102.7 (13.5) L· min^{-1} at 11km· h^{-1}.

Vertical jumping height, sprint 10m and 20 m improved after training by 5.0%, 3.3% and 1.6% ($p<0.001$), respectively (Table 2).

Table 2. Results from test of VO_{2max}, 1RM squat, vertical jump height and 20-m sprint

	VO_{2max}			Squats		
(n=21)	l · min^{-1}	ml · kg^{-1} · min^{-1}	ml · $kg^{-0.75}$ · min^{-1}	(kg)	(kg · m_b^{-1})	(kg · $m_b^{-0.67}$)
Pretraining	**4.73 ± 0.48**	**60.5 ± 4.8**	**178.4 ± 14.8**	**115.7 ± 23.1**	**1.5 ± 0.3**	**6.3 ± 1.3**
Posttraining	**5.21 ± 0.52**	**65.7 ± 5.22**	**192.9 ± 19.4**	**176.4 ± 18.2**	**2.2 ± 0.3**	**9.4 ± 1.0**

	Vertical jump	Sprint	
(n=21)	(cm)	10 m	20 m
Pretraining	**57.2 ±5.4**	**1.87 ± 0.06**	**3.13 ± 0.10**
Posttraining	**60.2 ± 5.4**	**1.81 ± 0.07**	**3.08 ± 0.09**

Neither VO_{2max} nor maximal strength (1RM) increased proportionally to body mass in elite soccer players. The exponent was found to be significantly less than unity, and the values were 0.70 ($r=0.66$, $p<0.001$) and 0.60 ($r=0.42$, $p<0.05$).

Squat 1RM became significantly correlated with jump height ($r=0.46$, $p<0.05$) and sprint 10m ($r=-0.43$, $p<0.05$) after the training period.

Discussion

The strength and endurance training intervention lead to a massive improvement in all physical tests related to the intervention, in a similar manner as when the strength and endurance interventions were carried out separately. The training effects for elite soccer players from the same relative training load is of similar magnitude as for lower level soccer players (Helgerud et al 2001; Hoff et al. 2002).

The change in 1RM half squats to a position with 90 degrees between femur and tibialis was on average 50.7 kg during the 8 weeks, 16 training sessions period. This equals 3.2 kg or 2.7% improvement per training session for the elite soccer players. The strength improvement from a session of 4 times 4 repetition using 85+ % of 1RM with emphasis on maximal mobilization of force in the concentric phase is similar to what was found for a group of lower level soccer players (Hoff et al. 2002). The strength response is higher than what is normally reported for trained hi-class professional athletes. The strength improvement of 49.2% took place with only 1 kg change in bodyweight, supporting the neural adaptation approach used by Almåsbakk & Hoff (1995), Behm & Sale (1993), Hoff & Almåsbakk (1996), Hoff et al. (2001), Sale (1992). A strong increase in strength per kg bodyweight follows from this response and would be expected to increase acceleration, following Newtons second law of motion. The results show a significant improvement in vertical jumping height of 3 cm or 5.0 %, in line with what has been shown from a similar intervention among World-Cup ski jumpers (Hoff et al. 2001). It is important to note that no specific jumping height training has been carried out except what has been implicit in the soccer play. Commonly used plyometrics show no comparable development in intervention experiments (Lees and Graham-Smith 1996). Similarly a highly significant improvement in sprinting times over 10m and 20m was shown. Initially there was no correlation between 1RM squats and 10m sprinting time. After the strength training intervention there is significant correlation between 1RM squat and 10m sprint performance. The improvement in sprinting time is equivalent to half a meter improvement over ten meters and are slightly less than expected from a previous study (Hoff 2001). No specific sprint training was carried out during the intervention period other than what is implicit in soccer play. Half a meter in ten meters still has practical implications in terms of trying to reach a ball before the opponent. No other single training intervention has shown similar improvements in sprinting performance. One reason why the sprinting result was a bit slower than what has been shown in a previous experiment might be that the team the day before the test returned from a two weeks pre-season training camp in Spain with one or two training sessions most of the days, and a couple of matches. The players complained from stiff legs, which normally influences high velocity performance. This might also be the reason why the 10 to 20 m time did not change from pre to posttest. Less control of the training and testing situation is however the price when carrying out high external validity research among elite soccer players.

Following the combined maximal strength and high intensity aerobic endurance interval training running economy improved significantly with 3.7 %. After having shown that maximal strength training gives improvements in work economy in an aerobic endurance performance in upper body work (Hoff et al. 1998, Hoff et al. 2002b), Hoff et al. (2002) have shown an improvement of 4.7 % for running economy following maximal strength squat training, after the same intervention as in this experiment with soccer players at a lower performance level as subjects. Also following interval endurance training as in this experiment, improvements in running economy by 6.7 % has been shown for 18 years old soccer players (Helgerud et al. 2001). The improvements from separate interventions gives a higher improvement in CR than the combined intervention in this experiment. One explanation might be a negative combined effect of the two interventions, but a more likely explanation is the complaint connected to stiff legs from high intensity soccer play during the Spain training camp.

The training intervention used to improve the aerobic endurance in this study increased VO2max with 5.2 $mL \cdot kg^{-1} \cdot min^{-1}$ or 8.1 %. This is in line with the 4.5% improvement with a similar training intervention alone in a study among 18 years old soccer players conducted by our research group (Helgerud et al. 2001). The improvement in VO_{2max} in this study occurs even if maximal strength training is carried out in the same training session, and shows that concurrent maximal strength and endurance training does not compromise aerobic endurance development. This improvement also occurs even though the players in this experiment have a higher VO_{2max} before start of the intervention, and are of a far higher performance level than the 18 years old players. The training response is equivalent to 0.54 % per interval training session. The training intervention took place after a 3 weeks brake since termination of the previous season. The players had been carrying out some endurance training to keep up their capacity, and show pre-test values that is normal at this level of performance (Reilly 1994, Davis et al. 1992, Nowacki et al. 1988, Rhodes et al. 1988, Thomas & Reilly 1979, White et al. 1988). If the goalkeepers are taken out of this material the average VO_{2max} for this group is 66.5±5.0 mL· kg^{-1} · min^{-1} in the posttest. Only Rosenborg FC, Trondheim, one of the few teams having participated in 7 European Champions League tournaments, have shown slightly higher values (Wisløff et al. 1998). In Wisløff et al. (1998) it is stated that near future development of soccer play will expect team values of 70 mL· kg^{-1} · min^{-1} and 200 kg in half squat strength. The recent World Championship strengthens this expectation for our research group, and we expect to see such figures in a relative near future.

Conclusions

There seem to be no negative effects from carrying out concurrent high intensity aerobic training and maximal strength training. In 8 weeks this Norwegian Premier League team show similar changes to what has been reported as top and bottom of the league (Wisløff et al. 1998). After the 8 week training intervention this team show test results equivalent to the highest values reported in the literature for a soccer team in terms of VO_{2max} and the highest values reported for a soccer team in terms of squat 1RM.

Practical applications

The practical applications from this study are that effective training interventions for maximal strength and aerobic endurance should be included in the pre-season training for top-level soccer teams. Our research group has previously shown the direct correlation between physical resources and soccer performance (Helgerud et al. 2001). The results from this study indicate that physical resources are relatively low in elite soccer players and seem to be holding back the performance level in international soccer.

References

Ali, A., and M.Farrally. (1991) A computer-video aided time-motion analysis technique for match analysis. *J Sports Med Phys Fit*, 1991, 31:82-88.

Almaasbakk, B. & Hoff,J., (1996*),* Coordination, the determinant of velocity Specificity. *J Appl Physiol*, 80(5): 2046-2052

Åstrand P.O. and Rodahl K. (1986) Textbook of Work Physiology. Physiological Basis of Exercise, 3rd edition. McGraw-Hill International Editions. New York.

Bangsbo, J. Time and motion characteristics of competiton soccer. Science and Football. 34-40. 1992.

Bangsbo, J., L. Nørregaard, and Thorsøe F. Activity profile of competition soccer. *Can J Sport Sci.*110-116. 1991.

Behm D.G. and Sale D.G. (1993b) Intended rather than actual movement velocity determines velocity-specific training response. *J Appl Physiol* 74(1):359-368

Bergh U., Sjødin B., Forsberg A. and Svedenhag J. (1991) The relationship between body mass and oxygen uptake during running in humans. *Med Sci Sports Exerc* 23:205-211

Bührle, M. and D. Schmidtbleicher. Der einfluss von maximalkrafttraining auf die bewegungsschnelligkeit (The influence of maximum strength training on movement velocity). *Leistungssport*, 7: 3-10, 1977.

Chromiak JA. and Mulvaney DR. A review: the effects of combined strength and endurance training on strength development. *J. Appl. Physiol.,* 4: 55-60, 1990.

Davis J.A., Brewer J., Atkin D. Pre-season physiological characteristics of English first and second division soccer players. *J. Sports Sci.* 10: 541-547, 1992.

Dudley G.A. and Djamil R. Incompatibility of endurance- and strength-training modes of exercise. *J Appl Physiol* 59:1446-1451. 1985.

Helgerud J. (1994) Maximal oxygen uptake, anaerobic threshold and running economy in women and men with similar performances level in marathons. *Eur. J. Appl. Physiol.* 68:155-161.

Helgerud, J., L.C. Engen, U. Wisløff, and J. Hoff. Aerobic endurance training improves soccer performance. *Med. Sci. Sports Exerc.* 33:1925-1931. 2001.

Hennessy L.C. and Watson A.W. (1994) The interference effects of training for strength and endurance simultaneously. *J Strength Cond Res* 8(1):12-19

Hoff, J., G.O.Berdahl, S. Bråten. Jumping height development and body weight considerations in ski jumping. In: Science and Skiing II, Müller, E., H. Schwameder, C. Raschner, S. Lidinger, E. Kornexl (eds), Verlag Dr. Kovac, Hamburg, 403-412, 2001.

Hoff, J. Training for rate of force development enhances running economy and aerobic performance. *Med Sci Sports Exerc.* 34: 5 Suppl: S270, 2001.

Hoff, J., J. Helgerud, U.Wisløff. Endurance training into the next millenium; Muscular strength training effects on aerobic endurance performance. *Am J Med Sports*, 4:58-67, 2002.

Hoff, J. and B. Almåsbakk. The effects of maximum strength training on throwing velocity and muscle strength in female team-handball players. *J. Strength Cond. Res.* 9: 255-258, 1995.

Hoff, J., U. Wisløff, L.C. Engen, O.J. Kemi, J. Helgerud. Soccer specific aerobic endurance training. *Br J Sports Med*, 36: 218-221, 2002.

Hoff J, Gran A, Helgerud J. Maximal strength training improves aerobic endurance performance. *Scand J Med Sci Sports*. 2002b, 12:2 (In press)

Lees A. and Graham-Smith P. (1996) Plyometric training: a review of principles and practice. *Sports Exerc Injury* 2:24-30

Nelson, A.G., D.A. Arnall, S.F. Loy, L.J. Silvester, and R.K. Conlee. Consequences of combining strength and endurance regimens. *Phys. Ther.,* 70: 287-294, 1990.

Nowacki PE., Cai DY., Buhl C., Krummelbein U. Biological performance of German soccer players (proffessionals and juniors) tested by special ergometry and treadmill methods. In: Science and Football, T Reilly, A Lees, K Davis, WJ Murphy (Eds.), London, Spon. 1988, pp. 145-157.

O'Donoghue, P. Time-motion analysis of work rate in elite soccer. In: Notational analysis of sport IV. M.H.a.F. Tavares. Centre for team sports studies, Faculty of Sport Sciences and Physical Education, University of Porto, Portugal: Porto, 2001. pp. 65-70.

Reilly, T. Motion analysis and physiological demands. In: Science and Soccer. R. T. E & FN Spon: London, 1996. pp. 65-79.

Reilly, T. Physiological profile of the player. In: Football (Soccer), Ekblom B (Ed.) Blackwell, London, pp. 78-94, 1994.

Reilly, T., and Thomas V. A motion analysis of work-rate in different positional roles in professional football match-play. *J. Hum. Mov Stud.* :87-97. 1976.

Rienzi, E., Drust B, Reilly T., Carter J.E.L., Martin A. Investigation of the anthropometric and work-rate profiles of elite South American international soccer players. *J Sports Med Phys Fitness.* 40:162-169. 2000.

Sale, D.G. Neural adaptations to strength training. In: Strength and power in sport. P.V. Komi (Ed.) Blackwell Scientific Publications, 1992, pp. 249-265.

Schmidtbleicher, D. Training for power events. In: Strength and power in sport. P. Komi (Ed.) Blackwell Scientific Publications, London, 381-395, 1992.

Smaros, G. Energy usage during football match. In: Proceedings of the first international congress on sports medicine applied to football. L. Vecchiet. : Rome, 1980. pp. 795-801.

Thomas V., Reilly T. Fitness assessment of English League soccer players throughout the competitive season. *Br J Sports Med.*, 13: 103-109, 1979.

Torvik, P.Ø., Helgerud, J. The validity of the portable metabolic test system Cortex Metamax. In Science and Skiing II. Müller E, Schwameder H (eds.) E & FN Spon, London, pp 641-654. 2001.

Valquer, W., Barros T.L., Sant'anna M. High intensity motion pattern analyses of Brazilian elite soccer players. In: IV World Congress of Notational Analysis of Sport. H.M. Tavares Fernanado. FCDEF-UP: Porto, Portugal, 1998. p. 80.

White JE, Emery TM., Kane JL., Grovers R., Risman AB. Pre-season fitness profiles of professional soccer players. In: Science and Football, T Reilly, A Lees, K Davis, WJ Murphy (Eds.) London, Spon, 1988, pp. 164-171.

Withers, R.T. Match analyses of Australian professional soccer players. *J Human Movement Studies.* 8:159-176. 1982.

Wisløff, U., J. Helgerud, and J. Hoff. Strength and endurance of elite soccer players. *Med. Sci. Sports Exerc.* 30:462-467. 1998.

ORIGINAL ARTICLE

Soccer specific aerobic endurance training

J Hoff, U Wisløff, L C Engen, O J Kemi, J Helgerud

Br J Sports Med 2002;**36**:218–221

See end of article for authors' affiliations

Correspondence to: Dr Hoff, Department of Physiology and Biomedical Engineering, Norwegian University of Science and Technology, N-7489 Trondheim, Norway; Jan.Hoff@medisin.ntnu.no

Accepted 3 December 2001

Background: In professional soccer, a significant amount of training time is used to improve players' aerobic capacity. However, it is not known whether soccer specific training fulfils the criterion of effective endurance training to improve maximal oxygen uptake, namely an exercise intensity of 90–95% of maximal heart rate in periods of three to eight minutes.
Objective: To determine whether ball dribbling and small group play are appropriate activities for interval training, and whether heart rate in soccer specific training is a valid measure of actual work intensity.
Methods: Six well trained first division soccer players took part in the study. To test whether soccer specific training was effective interval training, players ran in a specially designed dribbling track, as well as participating in small group play (five a side). Laboratory tests were carried out to establish the relation between heart rate and oxygen uptake while running on a treadmill. Corresponding measurements were made on the soccer field using a portable system for measuring oxygen uptake.
Results: Exercise intensity during small group play was 91.3% of maximal heart rate or 84.5% of maximal oxygen uptake. Corresponding values using a dribbling track were 93.5% and 91.7%. No higher heart rate was observed during soccer training.
Conclusions: Soccer specific exercise using ball dribbling or small group play may be performed as aerobic interval training. Heart rate monitoring during soccer specific exercise is a valid indicator of actual exercise intensity.

Physiological, technical, and tactical skills are all important to soccer performance. Factors such as acceleration, running velocity, jumping height, and capacity to release energy are of major importance. Because of the length of a soccer match, at least 90% of the energy release must be aerobic[1]; during a 90 minute match, players run about 10 km[2 3] at an intensity close to anaerobic threshold or 80–90% of maximal heart rate.[1 3 4]

Aerobic endurance performance is dependent on three important elements: maximal oxygen uptake (VO_2MAX), anaerobic threshold, and work economy.[5] VO_2MAX is defined as the highest oxygen uptake that can be achieved during dynamic exercise with large muscle groups.[6] Previous studies have shown a significant relation between VO_2MAX and distance covered during a match,[1 7] and a rank order correlation between VO_2MAX and placement in the league of the best teams in Hungary has been shown.[8] These findings are supported by Wisløff *et al*,[9] who have shown a substantial difference in VO_2MAX in members of the top team compared with those in the lowest placed team in the Norwegian elite league. Recently, Helgerud *et al*[3] showed that interval training (90–95% of maximal heart rate)—running uphill for four periods of four minutes, separated by three minutes active rest at 70% of maximal heart rate, twice a week over nine weeks—increased maximal oxygen uptake by 11% (from 58.1 ml/kg/min to 64.3 ml/kg/min). This resulted in a 20% increase in distance covered during a game, a 23% increase in involvement with the ball, and a 100% increase in the number of sprints, highlighting the advantages of a high VO_2MAX in soccer.

Anaerobic threshold is defined as the highest exercise intensity, heart rate, or oxygen uptake, working dynamically with large muscle groups, in which the production and clearance of lactate is about the same.[10] Anaerobic threshold in absolute terms (ml/kg/min) is important, but is highly dependent on VO_2MAX, and does not seem to change much in percentage of VO_2MAX. Owing to the length of a soccer game, the average exercise intensity cannot be much higher than that corresponding to anaerobic threshold. However, players do not actually exercise for long periods of the game at anaerobic threshold, but either above the threshold (accumulating lactate) or below the threshold (because of the need for lactate clearance).[3]

Work economy (C_R) is defined as oxygen cost at a submaximal exercise intensity, and as much as 20% difference in C_R has been found in trained endurance athletes at similar VO_2MAX level.[10] However, there is a paucity of research into the effect of improved C_R on soccer performance. Helgerud *et al*[3] showed that interval training increases C_R as VO_2MAX increases. Furthermore, a recent study showed that C_R could be improved by maximal strength training without improving VO_2MAX.[11] This approach could be used in future studies to determine the effects of exclusively improved C_R on soccer performance.

Running is usually not the favourite activity of soccer players. However, playing soccer is not believed to provide sufficient exercise intensity over time to improve VO_2MAX very much.[3 9] During interval training, as reported by Helgerud *et al*,[3] intensity is normally monitored and controlled by hear rate monitors. During a game of soccer, however, concentrating on team players and opponents and controlling the ball, or anxiety caused by training or match situations, may lead to heart rates above what reflects the actual workload.[12 13] To achieve valid exercise intensities in soccer specific training, the relation between heart rate and oxygen uptake has to be established.

The aim of this study was to (*a*) design a dribbling track and a playing session that fulfils our criterion of effective aerobic interval training, and (*b*) determine whether heart rate is a valid measure of work intensity in soccer specific endurance training.

METHODS

Subjects

Six male soccer players from a Norwegian first division team volunteered to participate in the three different training modes. Before the study, each subject reviewed and signed consent forms in accordance with the Declaration of Helsinki and the

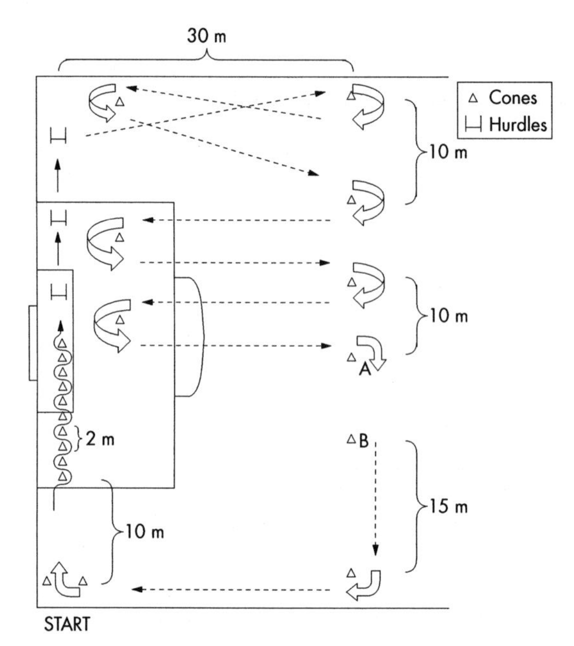

Figure 1 Soccer specific "dribbling track" for measuring maximal oxygen uptake (VO_2MAX). The ball is dribbled in the direction of the arrows, with backward running between points A and B. Subjects were instructed to gradually increase intensity to a level that brought them to VO_2MAX within six minutes.

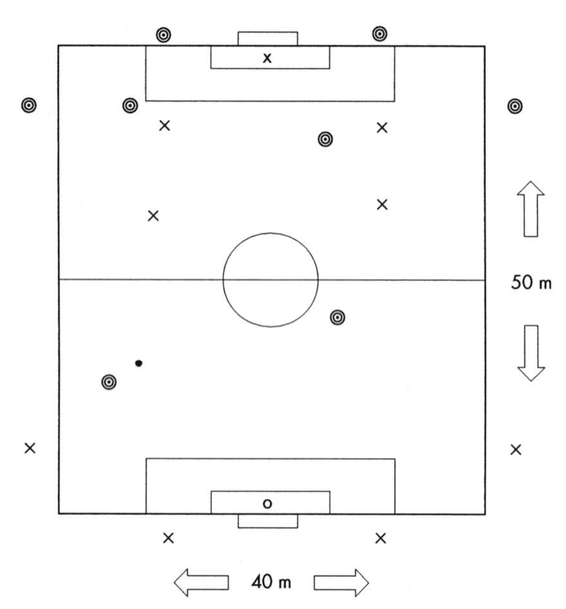

Figure 2 Small group play: five a side football, including a goalkeeper. Several balls were stored in each goal so that they could be rapidly introduced into play to avoid stoppages. Two resting players on each team assisted the playing team by acting as a "wall" on the sidelines of the attacking half of the field.

human research review committee of the Norwegian University of Science and Technology. Subjects were informed about the test protocols, without being informed about the aim of the study. The mean (SD) age of the soccer players was 22.2 (3.3) years, weight was 77.5 (12.4) kg, height was 180.2 (5.5) cm, and maximal heart rate was 198.3 (5.5) beats/min. The laboratory tests were carried out first, and the dribbling course and small group play were carried out in randomised order.

Testing

Laboratory tests

All laboratory tests were performed on the same day. Room temperature was 21–22°C and relative humidity was 50%. Subjects carried out a 20 minute warm up at 50–60% of VO_2MAX, running on a treadmill. VO_2MAX was determined with the treadmill inclined at 3° (Jaeger LE 5000; Erich Jaeger GmbH, Germany), as described previously.[10] Briefly, running speed was increased by 1 km/h every minute to a level that brought the subjects to VO_2MAX after about five minutes. VO_2MAX was defined as levelling off of oxygen uptake despite increased exercise intensity, and unhaemolysed blood lactate concentration above 6 mmol/l. Immediately after VO_2MAX determination, each subject ran for two minutes at an exercise intensity of 50–60% of VO_2MAX directly followed by a supramaximal intensity run, which resulted in exhaustion within three minutes. The highest heart rate (f_c), measured by short range radiotelemetry (Polar Sporttester; Polar Electro, Oy, Finland) during the last minute of running, was recorded as f_{cmax}. Oxygen uptake, ventilation (VE), respiratory exchange ratio (R), and breathing frequency (f_b) were measured using an Ergooxyscreen Sprint (EOS; Erich Jaeger). Unhaemolysed blood lactate was determined using a lactate analyser (YSI Model 1500 Sport Lactate Analyzer; Yellow Springs Instruments Co, Yellow Springs, Ohio, USA).

Dribbling track

The field running test measurements were performed a minimum of three days and a maximum of nine days after the laboratory test on an indoor high quality soccer field consisting of artificial curled nylon grass filled with sand. All field tests were performed after a 30 minute soccer training warm up period. Figure 1 shows the dribbling track for the endurance training.

The soccer players dribbled the ball through the cones and lifted the ball over the 30 cm high hurdles. Between point A and B the players moved backwards while controlling the ball, before turning and starting on a new round. Players were instructed to increase running intensity gradually to a level that brought them to 90–95% of maximal heart rate after about 60 seconds in the four minute training bout. The players carried out two four minute intervals, separated by a three minute exercise at 70% of maximal heart rate. Heart rate was monitored using Polar heart rate monitors which were continuously observable by the player during the run. The player was also assisted in assessing heart rate by the test leader observing the heart rate transmitted by telemetry (Polar Sport Tester). One person replaced cones and hurdles that fell down. VO_2, VE, R, and f_b were measured using the portable metabolic test system Metamax II (MMX II) (Cortex Metamax, Leipzig, Germany). The MMX II has been shown to be valid, reliable, and comparable to the EOS used in the laboratory test.[14]

Small group play

Small group play was organised as five a side, including goalkeepers as shown in fig 2. Pilot studies indicated that it would be necessary to use four minute periods of play to reach at least three minutes in the high intensity zone. Intensity was sought to be as high as possible through the four minute playing periods. Two four minute playing periods were carried out, separated by three minutes of active rest. Pilot studies showed that active coaching by encouragement and constructive messages was necessary to achieve a high enough intensity for some of the players. The measuring equipment was similar to that used for the dribbling track.

Table 1 Comparison of respiratory variables between laboratory test and field training

	Laboratory max test	Dribbling track	Small group play
f_c (beats/min)	198.3 (7.9)	185.5 (6.7)	181.0 (4.4)*
Vo_2 (litres/min)	5.22 (0.68)	4.74 (0.53)	4.42 (0.61)
Vo_2 (ml/kg/min)	67.8 (7.6)	62.2 (5.0)	57.3 (3.9)
Vo_2 (ml/0.75 kg/min)	200.4 (19.4)	181.8 (10.5)	171.8 (10.0)
Th_{an} (ml/kg/min)	50.9 (4.0)		
Th_{an} (ml/0.75 kg/min)	150.4 (7.7)		
Th_{an} (beats/min)	178.3 (8.8)		
R (Vco_2/Vo_2)	1.16 (0.07)	0.99 (0.07)	0.94 (0.07)
VE (litres/min)	174.6 (20.7)	138.7 (21.3)	132.0 (15.3)
f_b (breaths/min)	55.8 (6.4)	49.6 (2.8)	48.8 (7.2)

Data are mean (SD).
Vo_2MAX, Maximal oxygen uptake; f_{cmax}, maximal heart rate; f_{bmax}, maximal breathing frequency; VE, ventilation; R, respiratory exchange ratio; Vco_2, carbon dioxide output; Vo_2, oxygen uptake; Th_{an}, anaerobic threshold.
*Significantly different from value obtained on dribbling track, $p<0.05$. All training and soccer play values are significantly different from the laboratory max test.

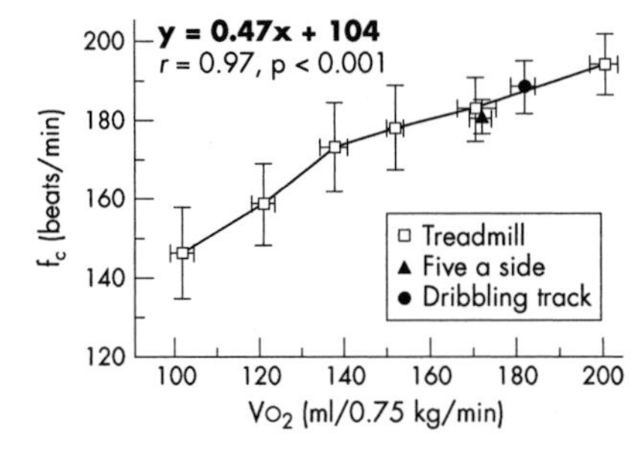

Figure 3 Correlation between Vo_2 and f_c at different submaximal velocities during treadmill testing ($r = 0.844$, $p<0.01$). A linear regression is shown.

Statistical analysis

Data are expressed as means (SD). The Kruskall-Wallis test was used to evaluate differences between tests. Spearman correlation coefficients were used when appropriate. Cautious calculations from previous studies[3 9] and pilot experiments showed that six players were enough to test the hypothesis with a statistical power of 0.90 ($p<0.05$).

RESULTS

During small group play, exercise intensity was 91.3% of f_{cmax} or 84.5% of Vo_2MAX. Corresponding intensity in the dribbling track was 93.5% of f_{cmax} or 91.7% of Vo_2MAX. f_c corresponding to 90–95% of f_{cmax} was reached after 61.5 (10.8) seconds on the dribbling track, and after 62.5 (12.5) seconds in small group play (table 1).

Figure 3 shows the relation between Vo_2 and f_c measured at several submaximal intensities on the treadmill (correlation coefficient $r = 0.844$, $p<0.01$). The Vo_2-f_c relation in either of the soccer specific training situations was not significantly different from running on the treadmill (fig 3). f_c was higher on the dribbling track than during small group play ($p<0.05$).

Average Vo_2 and the corresponding f_c were similar in both playing sessions, whereas, during the dribbling course, Vo_2 was significantly ($p<0.05$) reduced by 3.9%, with unchanged f_c in the second interval. The players with the highest Vo_2MAX showed the lowest percentage of Vo_2MAX during the small group play.

DISCUSSION

The major finding of this study is that specifically designed soccer training fulfils the criteria for aerobic interval training. Furthermore, heart rate monitoring is a valid measure of actual exercise intensity in these types of training modes.

The results therefore show that it is possible to perform soccer specific endurance training in the form of specially designed small group play or on a dribbling track, within the intensity zone for effectively developing Vo_2MAX and corresponding soccer performance.[3] It should be emphasised that this requires good organisation, as satisfactory exercise intensity was not reached during small group play without active coaching—that is, constructive instructions and encouragement to the players when necessary. Several factors must be considered when designing soccer specific aerobic endurance training. Firstly, intensity has to be higher than in normal soccer matches. This can be achieved by altering the number of players and field size and reducing the time the ball is out of play.[1] The fact that players with the highest Vo_2MAX had the lowest percentage of Vo_2MAX during small group play indicates that the playing situation designed for this experiment may have a ceiling effect for developing aerobic endurance. Therefore, players with a high Vo_2MAX may have to train on the dribbling track because higher exercise intensity is achievable in this way than during small group play, or they may have to run uphill to have the same training response as players with lower Vo_2MAX.

A problem to be considered when designing a dribbling track is that soccer is played on a flat surface, and research has shown that subjects running on a flat surface may not be able to reach exercise intensities close to Vo_2MAX.[14] Therefore, Vo_2MAX is usually measured with the treadmill at a 3° inclination. In the design of the dribbling track, the inclination should be compensated for by changes in pace and direction, both of which increase workload.

Intermittent work—that is, part of the time is spent standing still, as seen in soccer play—may overestimate Vo_2 based on f_c measurements compared with a continuous workload. The dribbling track should therefore be designed to be continuous, but allow for some variation in exercise intensity. Previously, the measuring equipment has been too complicated for field testing of soccer players, both in terms of weight and size. Smaller and lighter (800 g) equipment—for example, Metamax Cortex II—has been tested in our laboratory and found to be valid, reliable, and comparable to the EOS Sprint used for the laboratory measurements.[15]

On the dribbling track, the soccer players could have exercised at an intensity considerably higher than that shown in this experiment. In fact, in line with observations from running training (without a ball), the players had to be told to reduce their intensity in the first interval, so as not to exceed the planned intensity of 90–95% of f_{cmax}. Higher exercise intensities lead to increased lactate levels and a lower aerobic training response, and often result in fatigue and failure to complete the planned training session. A work intensity of 90–95% of f_{cmax} is higher than the anaerobic threshold. Activity during pauses is thus important to reduce lactate build up in the muscles and subsequently in the blood.[16] The high intensity—close to V_{O_2}MAX—also limits the length of the working periods and the number of intervals that it is possible to carry out. Helgerud *et al*[3] used 4 × 4 minute intervals, which seemed to be very effective for soccer players with a V_{O_2}MAX in the range 55–65 ml. Better trained subjects would probably have optimised training responses through somewhat longer interval periods or a higher number of intervals, and the opposite is probably true for less trained subjects.

The soccer players in this experiment showed a higher V_{O_2}MAX than that reported previously,[4] but in line with results reported by Wisløff *et al*.[9] However, the players in our study do not represent a whole team, and, as volunteers for an endurance experiment, they probably have a genetic predisposition for endurance performance. Therefore, the V_{O_2}MAX results cannot be generalised to all groups of soccer players. Monitoring heart rate during play would give the coach valuable information about training effects.

Conclusions

High intensity, aerobic, endurance, interval training can be carried out in a more soccer specific way than plain running. A specially designed dribbling track and small group play can produce the intended work intensity. Heart rate is shown to be a valid and reliable indicator of oxygen uptake in small group play with no, or only short, stops, as well as on the dribbling track, as shown in this experiment.

Authors' affiliations
J Hoff, U Wisløff, L C Engen, O J Kemi, J Helgerud, Department of Physiology and Biomedical Engineering, Norwegian University of Science and Technology, N-7489 Trondheim, Norway

REFERENCES

1 **Bangsbo J**. Energy demands in competitive soccer. *J Sports Sci* 1994;**12**(special no):S5–12.
2 **Bangsbo J**, Nørregaard L, Thorsøe F. Activity profile of competition soccer. *Can J Sport Sci* 1991;**16**:110–16.
3 **Helgerud J**, Engen LC, Wisløff U, *et al*. Aerobic endurance training improves soccer performance. *Med Sci Sports Exerc* 2001;**33**:1925–31.
4 **Reilly T**, Ball D. The net physiological cost of dribbling a soccer ball. *Res Q Exerc Sport* 1984;**55**:267–71.
5 **Pate RR**, Kriska A. Physiological basis of the sex difference in cardiorespiratory endurance. *Sports Med* 1984;**1**:87–98.
6 **Wagner PD**. Determinants of maximal oxygen transport and utilization. *Annu Rev Physiol* 1996;**58**:21–50.
7 **Smaros G**. Energy usage during a football match. In: Vecciet L, ed. *Proceedings of the First International Congress on Sports Medicine Applied to Football*. Rome: Guanillo, D, 1980:795–801.
8 **Apor P**. Successful formulae for fitness training. In: Reilly T, Lees A, Davids K, *et al*, eds. *Science and football*. London: E & F N Spon, 1988:95–107.
9 **Wisloff U**, Helgerud J, Hoff J. Strength and endurance of elite soccer players. *Med Sci Sports Exerc* 1998;**30**:462–7.
10 **Helgerud J**, Ingjer F, Stromme SB. Sex differences in performance-matched marathon runners. *Eur J Appl Physiol* 1990;**61**:433–9.
11 **Hoff J**, Helgerud J, Wisloff U. Maximal strength training improves work economy in trained female cross-country skiers. *Med Sci Sports Exerc* 1999;**31**:870–7.
12 **Blix AS**, Stromme SB, Ursin H. Additional heart rate: an indicator of psychological activation. *Aerosp Med* 1974;**45**:1219–22.
13 **Herd JA**. Cardiovascular response to stress. *Physiol Rev* 1991;**71**:305–30.
14 **Åstrand PO**, Rodahl K. *Textbook of work physiology*. New York: McGraw-Hill, 1986.
15 **Torvik PØ**, Helgerud J. The validity of the portable metabolic test system Cortex Metamax. In: Müller E, ed. *Science and skiing II*. Hamburg: Verlag Dr Kovaç 2001:641–54.
16 **Hermansen L**, Stensvold I. Production and removal of lactate during exercise in man. *Acta Physiol Scand* 1972;**86**:191–201.

Take home message

The single most important physiological parameter that describes the amount of work carried out during a soccer match is maximal oxygen uptake, which is most effectively trained at an intensity of 90–95% of maximal heart rate, normally by running. By using small group play and a specifically designed dribbling track, soccer players, who are more readily motivated by playing with a ball, no longer need to carry out plain running to improve their maximal oxygen uptake.

Editorial office address

Please note that the editorial office of *British Journal of Sports Medicine* has moved. Please send all future communications to: Dr Paul McCrory, *British Journal of Sports Medicine,* Centre for Sports Medicine Research & Education, School of Physiotherapy, Level 1, 200 Berkeley Street, Parkville, Victoria 3052, Australia;
Tel: +61 3 8344 4118; Fax: +61 3 8344 3771;
Email: bjsm@BMJgroup.com

Accepted for publication in: The Journal of Sports Medicine and Physical Fitness

SOCCER SPECIFIC TESTING OF MAXIMAL OXYGEN UPTAKE.

Ole Johan Kemi, Jan Hoff, Lars Christian Engen, Jan Helgerud and Ulrik Wisløff.

Department of Physiology and Biomedical Engineering, Faculty of Medicine, Medical Technology Center, Norwegian University of Science and Technology, N-7489 Trondheim, Norway.

Abstract

Background: Endurance capacity in soccer players is important. A soccer specific test for direct measurement of maximal oxygen uptake does, however, not exist. The aim of this study was to evaluate maximal oxygen uptake in a soccer specific field test, compared to treadmill running. **Methods:** Ten male soccer players (age 21.9 ± 3.0 years, body mass 73.3 ± 9.5 kg, height 179.9 ± 4.7 cm) participated in the study, and five endurance trained men (age 24.9 ± 1.8 years, body mass 81.5 ± 3.7 kg, height 185.6 ± 3.1 cm) took part in a comparison of the portable and the stationary metabolic test systems. The soccer players accomplished a treadmill test and a soccer specific field test containing dribbling, repetitive jumping, accelerations, decelerations, turning and backwards running. **Results:** Maximal oxygen uptake was similar in field (5.0 ± 0.5 $L \cdot min^{-1}$) and laboratory (5.1 ± 0.7 $L \cdot min^{-1}$) tests, as were maximal heart rate, maximal breathing frequency, respiratory exchange ratio and oxygen pulse. Maximal ventilation was 5.4 % higher at maximal oxygen uptake during treadmill running. **Conclusions:** These findings show that testing of maximal oxygen uptake during soccer specific testing gives similar results as during treadmill running, and therefore serves as a valid test of maximal oxygen uptake in soccer players.

Key words: Field test, portable test system, Cortex Metamax II, maximal oxygen consumption, aerobic capacity.

Introduction

The standard method for measuring maximal oxygen uptake (VO_{2max}) of soccer players is by treadmill tests. However, most laboratories have experienced that it might be problematic to attract the best players into laboratory tests, due to motivational reasons. Several sport specific field tests (e.g. 1;2;3;4;5;6;7;8;9) exists that estimate maximal oxygen uptake (VO_{2max}) of executors, normally with an accuracy of ± 10-15 % (10). The development of small portable metabolic test systems has made it possible to measure oxygen uptake (VO_2) directly during soccer specific tests. It has previously been shown that an inclined treadmill recruits a larger muscle mass and a slower cadence which allows the individual to reach the true VO_{2max}, compared to running on the flat (10). However, it is anticipated that the additional oxygen demand during ball dribbling in soccer-like movements compensates for the extra load of the inclined treadmill, as applied during standard laboratory tests of VO_{2max}. Thus, the aim of the present study was to compare VO_{2max} obtained in a soccer specific field test with values obtained from treadmill running.

Materials and Methods

Ten male soccer players from a Norwegian first division team participated in the soccer specific testing. It seems to be an established practice to use a stationary metabolic system when testing VO_2 in the laboratory and a portable system during field testing. We chose therefore a stationary system in the laboratory (Ergooxyscreen Sprint (EOS), Erich Jaeger GmbH, Germany), and a portable system in the field (Metamax II (MMX II), Cortex Biophysik GmbH, Germany). Therefore, in a preliminary study five endurance trained men that were familiar with physical testing took part in the comparison of MMX II and EOS, which has been previously validated against the Douglas bag method (11).

To compare the metabolic systems, endurance athletes were tested by the same protocol with both metabolic test systems in random order. No subjects received any information on their results before both tests were carried out. The MMX II was demonstrated to give similar oxygen uptake values as when using EOS, in line with what has been shown for the previous version of the apparatus (12). Results of comparing EOS and MMX II are presented in Figure 1 and Table 1.

Figure 1

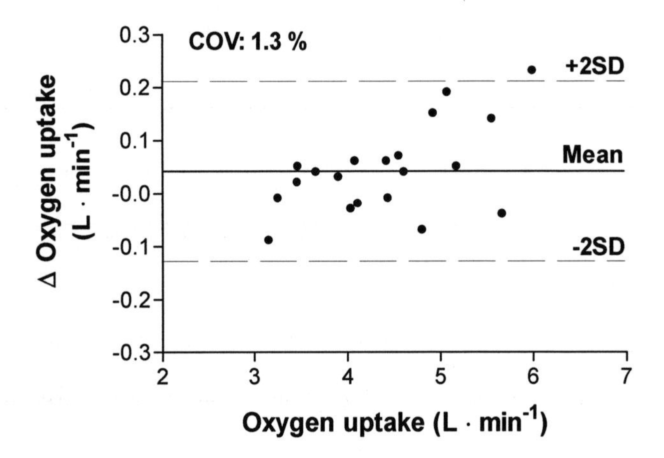

Figure 1. Difference between oxygen uptake measured with Ergooxyscreen Sprint and Metamax II test systems (Δ Oxygen uptake).

Data are individual differences between the two apparatus' of 5 subjects, that are conducted during treadmill running, at 6° inclination, 6.5, 8, 9.5 km · hour^{-1} in five minute periods and incremental running to exhaustion. COV: Coefficient of variation.

Table 1. Comparison between Ergooxyscreen Sprint and Metamax II test systems.

		Running speed			
		6.5 km · hour^{-1}	**8 km · hour^{-1}**	**9.5 km · hour^{-1}**	**Maximal**
***V*O$_2$**	L · min^{-1}				
	EOS	3.41 ± 0.22	4.12 ± 0.20	4.77 ± 0.32	5.47 ± 0.51
	MMX II	3.40 ± 0.18	4.10 ± 0.18	4.71 ± 0.29	5.38 ± 0.45
V_E	L · min^{-1}				
	EOS	76.4 ± 4.5	98.8 ± 5.5	132.7 ± 11.7	180.9 ± 24.1
	MMX II	74.6 ± 5.1	95.9 ± 6.9	125.6 ± 8.0	173.9 ± 24.5
f_b	Breaths · min^{-1}				
	EOS	32.8 ± 4.6	36.0 ± 3.2	41.6 ± 6.2	56.4 ± 2.7
	MMX II	31.8 ± 5.0	34.6 ± 5.2	41.8 ± 6.5	60.0 ± 2.7
R	$VCO_2 \cdot VO_2^{-1}$				
	EOS	0.93 ± 0.03	0.96 ± 0.02	1.00 ± 0.01	1.15 ± 0.04
	MMX II	0.94 ± 0.02	0.98 ± 0.01	1.02 ± 0.02	1.15 ± 0.04

Data are mean and standard deviation from 5 subjects. Running was performed at 6° treadmill inclination for five minutes at submaximal stages, and to exhaustion at maximal stage. VO_2: oxygen uptake, V_E: ventilation, f_b: breathing frequency, EOS: ergooxyscreen sprint, MMX II: metamax II, R: respiratory exchange ratio, VCO_2: carbon dioxide output, VO_2: oxygen uptake.

Each subject reviewed and signed consent forms prior to the study, and protocols were in accordance with the Declaration of Helsinki; recommendations guiding physicians in biomedical research involving human subjects. Subjects were informed about the test protocols, but not about the aim of the study. The mean age, body mass and height of the soccer players were 21.9 ± 3.0 years, 73.3 ± 9.5 kg, and 179.9 ± 4.7 cm, respectively, while the endurance athletes were 24.2 ± 1.8 years, 81.5 ± 3.7 kg, and 185.6 ± 3.1 cm, respectively.

All soccer players were tested on the same day in a laboratory with a room temperature of 21-22° C and relative humidity of 50 %. Five of the players had one week earlier performed the field test as described below. Subjects performed 20 minutes warm up at approximately 50-60 % of VO_{2max}, running on a treadmill (Jaeger LE 5000, Erich Jaeger GmbH, Germany). The VO_{2max} was determined during treadmill running at 3° inclination, as previously described (13). Briefly, running speed was increased by 1 km · hour^{-1} every minute to a level that brought the subjects to exhaustion after about 6 minutes. The highest heart rate, measured by short-range radio telemetry (Polar Sporttester, Polar Electro Oy., Finland) during the last minute of running was defined as maximal heart rate. The VO_2, ventilation, respiratory exchange ratio and breathing frequency were measured using the EOS (Erich Jaeger GmbH., Germany). A levelling off of VO_2 despite increased running speed, respiratory exchange ratio above 1.05, and heart rate less than 10 beats · min^{-1} from maximal heart rate were used as criteria for reaching VO_{2max}.

The field measurements were performed on a high quality indoor soccer field consisting of artificial curled nylon grass filed with sand. The field test for measuring VO_{2max} is shown in Figure 2.

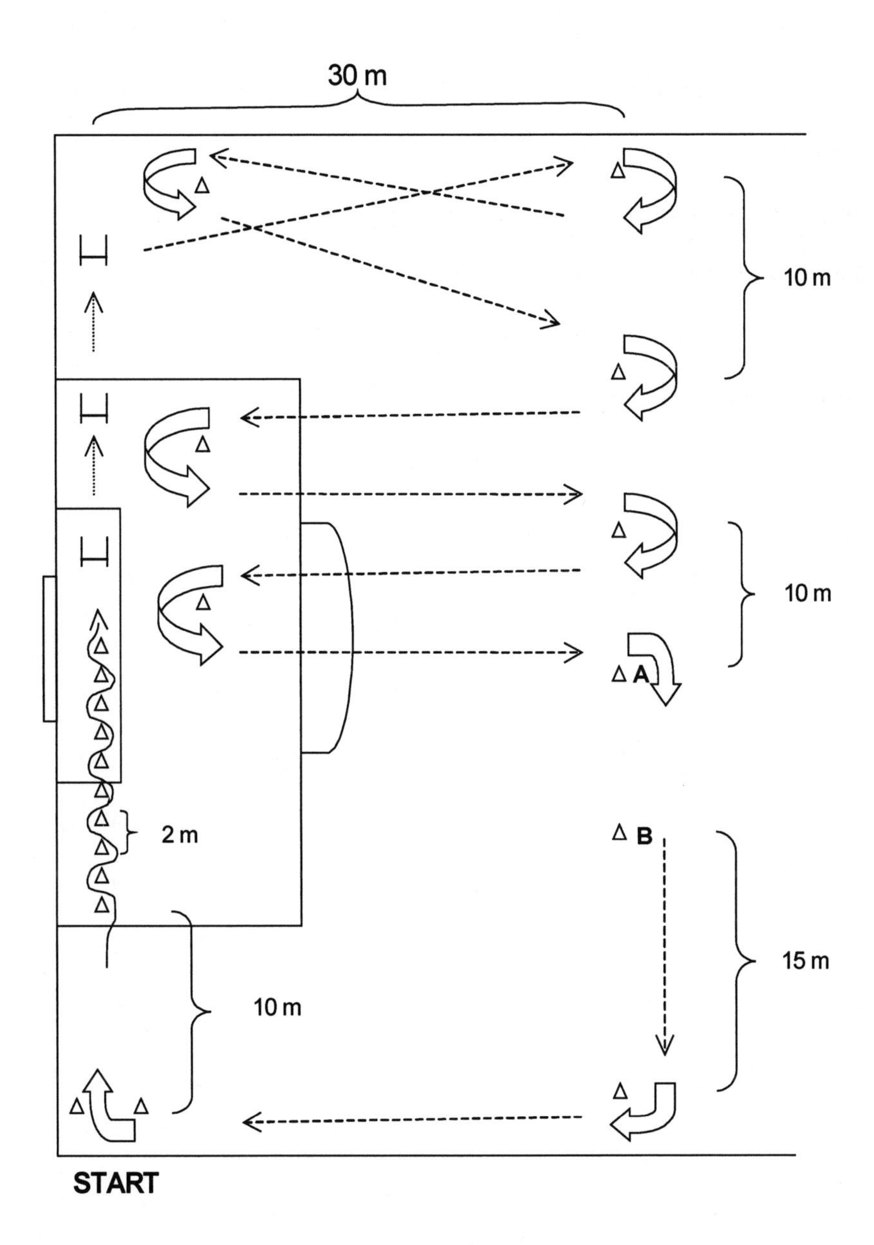

Figure 2. Soccer specific field test for maximal oxygen uptake.

The field route follows the arrows by dribbling a ball. Backward running between point A and B. Subjects were instructed to gradually increase intensity to a level that brought the subjects to maximal oxygen uptake within six minutes. △: Cones, ⊢⊣ : hurdles.

The soccer players dribbled the ball through the cones and lifted it over the 30 cm high hurdles. Between point A and B players dribbled backwards, before turning and starting on a new round. Players were instructed to increase running intensity gradually to a running intensity corresponding to about 95 % of maximal heart rate (normally reached after about 2 minutes), which was maintained for 3 minutes, before increasing the running speed to a level that brought the subjects to exhaustion after about 6 minutes (total test time 6-8 minutes).

Pilot-studies revealed this particular course and protocol to yield the highest VO_2. One person took care of the cones and hurdles that fell down. Heart rate was measured as described above. Oxygen uptake, ventilation, respiratory exchange ratio and breathing frequency were measured using the portable metabolic test system MMX II. A levelling off of oxygen uptake despite increased heart rate and heart rate less than 10 beats · min^{-1} from maximal heart rate was used as criterion of reaching VO_{2max}.

Results are reported as means and standard deviations. Wilcoxon matched pairs signed rank sum test was used to determine differences between the MMX II and EOS, as well as between laboratory and field measurements. Coefficients of variation were also analysed to compare the MMX II and EOS, as well as laboratory and field measurements, together with the measurement method comparison as described by Bland and Altman (14). Linear regression was used to determine the relationship between VO_2 and f_c during treadmill running. Spearman Rank correlation coefficient was calculated where appropriate. Linear regression was used to Significance was set at $p < 0.05$.

Results

The $\dot{V}O_{2max}$, maximal heart rate, maximal breathing frequency, respiratory exchange ratio and oxygen pulse were not different in laboratory and field tests (Figure 3 and Table 2). As described in Figure 3, following the suggestions of Bland and Altman (14), there is a good agreement between the laboratory and the field tests, within +/- 2 standard deviation, and with a coefficient of variation of 4.8 %. Maximal ventilation at maximal oxygen uptake was 5.4 % lower ($p < 0.05$) in the field test compared to the laboratory test. Figure 4 shows the relationship (linear regression: $r = 0.84$, $p < 0.01$) between $\dot{V}O_2$ and heart rate at increasing exercise intensities during treadmill running. It further shows that this relationship at 95 % of maximal heart rate during the field test corresponds to that observed during treadmill running.

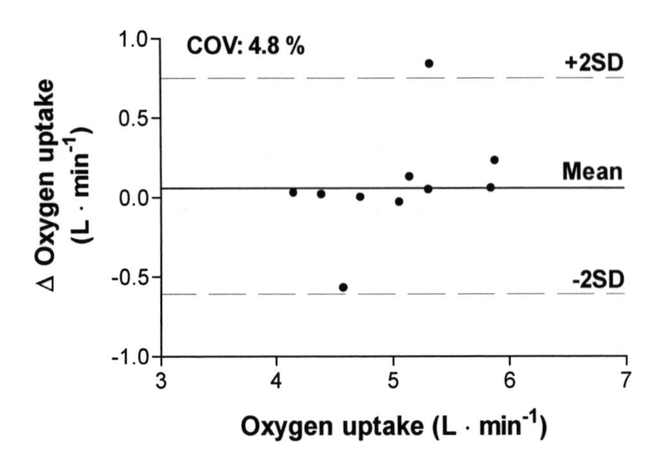

Figure 3. Difference between oxygen uptake measured in the laboratory and on the field (Δ Oxygen uptake).

Data are individual differences between the laboratory and the field test of 10 subjects. COV: Coefficient of variation.

Table 2. Comparison between laboratory and field test.

		Laboratory test	Field test
VO_{2max}	$L \cdot min^{-1}$	5.08 ± 0.67	5.00 ± 0.53
	$mL \cdot kg^{-1} \cdot min^{-1}$	65.6 ± 7.1	65.7 ± 5.1
	$mL \cdot kg^{-0.75} \cdot min^{-1}$	193.3 ± 19.0	194.4 ± 13.5
f_{cmax}	$beats \cdot min^{-1}$	197 ± 8	195 ± 7
f_{bmax}	$breaths \cdot min^{-1}$	55.4 ± 5.9	57.9 ± 4.7
V_E	$L \cdot min^{-1}$	162.2 ± 25.2 *	153.4 ± 20.9
R	$VCO_2 \cdot VO_2^{-1}$	1.16 ± 0.05	1.12 ± 0.05

Data are mean and standard deviation from 10 subjects. VO_{2max}: maximal oxygen uptake, f_{cmax}: maximal heart rate, f_{bmax}: maximal breathing frequency, V_E: ventilation, R: respiratory exchange ratio, VCO_2: carbon dioxide output, VO_2: oxygen uptake. *: Significantly different, $p < 0.05$.

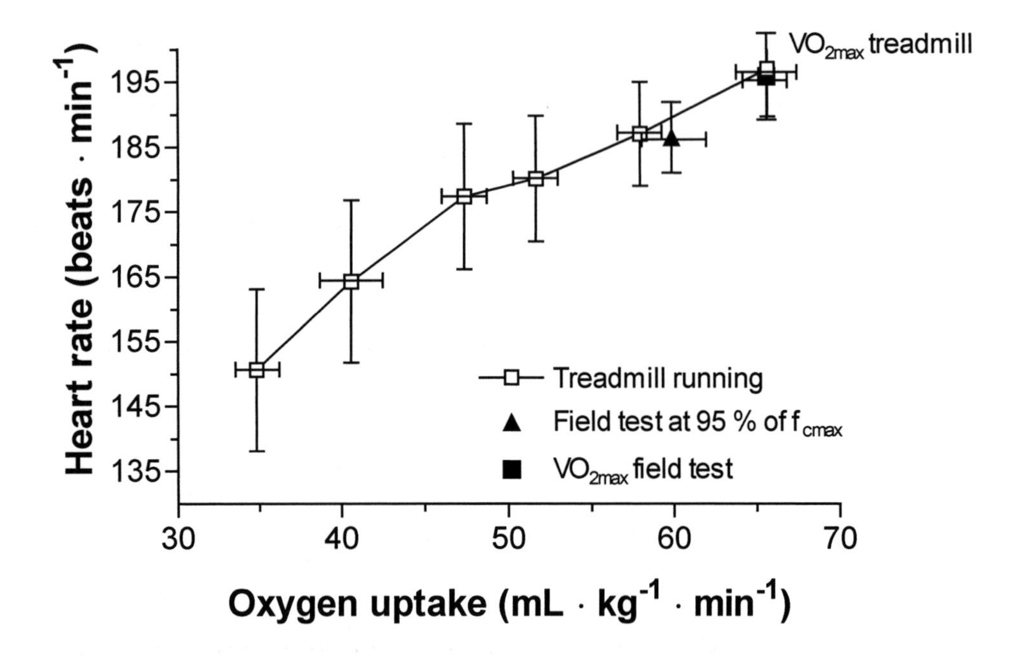

Figure 4. Oxygen uptake and heart rate relationship at submaximal and maximal intensity during treadmill running and field test.

Data are mean and standard deviations from 10 subjects. Measurements are conducted during submaximal and maximal treadmill running (white marks), and at 95 % of maximal heart rate and maximal intensity ($\dot{V}O_{2max}$) at field test (black marks).

Discussion

This is the first study to show that a soccer specific field test gives similar values of $\dot{V}O_{2max}$ as when running on the treadmill. Thus, the additional oxygen demand during ball dribbling, jumping, accelerating, decelerating, turning and backwards running (2;15;16) substitutes for the extra load of the inclined treadmill when testing $\dot{V}O_{2max}$ in the laboratory. Despite the two test regimens serving as equal tools, the soccer players felt the field test to be more motivating. However, the motivation was however not measured, and the players' comments serve thus only as an indication. It should though be pointed out that treadmill testing in the laboratory gives more standardized conditions to study the parameters of interest, for instance running economy at sub-maximal exercise intensities and anaerobic threshold, as when compared to field tests.

When testing $\dot{V}O_{2max}$, a levelling-off in $\dot{V}O_2$ despite increased exercise intensity as well as a respiratory exchange ratio above 1.05 was observed both in the laboratory and the field tests. It is therefore suggested that these criteria should be met also when testing $\dot{V}O_{2max}$ using the present field test.

Between the second and fifth minute of the field test, the steady state exercise intensity was on average 95.2 % of maximal heart rate, corresponding to 86.5 % of $\dot{V}O_{2max}$. These values are within an effective zone for development of $\dot{V}O_{2max}$, and corresponding soccer performance (17). Thus, this type of exercise could serve as soccer specific activity that is suitable for developing $\dot{V}O_{2max}$.

There was a consistent linear relationship between $\dot{V}O_2$ and heart rate during treadmill running at increasing intensities. At exercise intensities above 90 % of maximal heart rate, the $\dot{V}O_2$ and heart rate relationship on the field test corresponds to that observed during treadmill running (Figure 4). Thus, at high exercise intensities, heart rate should therefore be a valid measure to guide intensity during soccer specific training.

In the present study, $\dot{V}O_{2max}$ is higher than most other reports of soccer players, since $\dot{V}O_{2max}$ is regularly reported in the range of 55 and 68 $mL \cdot kg^{-1} \cdot min^{-1}$ in international level soccer players (18-22). These reports are, however, covering the last decades, so they may reflect a change in training regimens too. This makes it difficult to compare directly the different studies regarding $\dot{V}O_{2max}$. The importance of a high $\dot{V}O_{2max}$ is demonstrated in several reports (17;18;22).

Lower maximal ventilation in the field test might reflect that $\dot{V}O_{2max}$ could be reached without reaching maximal ventilation (23). Furthermore, it might be harder to work to exhaustion, and thereby maximal ventilation, when simultaneously performing technical soccer skills. The trend towards lower respiratory exchange ratio found in the field test supports the assumption that it might be harder to work to complete exhaustion during the field test. This implies that it during the treadmill protocol could be possible to derive more energy from anaerobic sources than in the field test, an anaerobiosis that would be associated with increased ventilation.

Respiratory exchange ratio is, however, well above the criteria for reaching $\dot{V}O_{2max}$ in all tests. Nor can it be excluded that the difference in maximal ventilation could be due to the fact that the measurements were made with a mouthpiece (EOS) and a facemask (MMX II) in the laboratory and field test, respectively. However, breathing frequency was similar both in the comparison of the equipment (Table 1) and in the field vs. laboratory protocols (Table 2). Due to the trend towards lower maximal ventilation using MMX II, and the low number of subjects in the comparison protocol in the present study, the need for appropriate validation of MMX II is necessitated if measuring higher ventilation than in the present study.

Conclusion

The present soccer-specific test was found to be valid for measuring $\dot{V}O_{2max}$, and thus serves as an alternative for the traditional treadmill test. The existence of a valid soccer-specific test might lead to more frequent testing, allowing a proper control and development of the individual players $\dot{V}O_{2max}$. However, the test is not standardised enough to measure anaerobic threshold and work economy, which still should be determined in the laboratory.

References

1. Balsom, P.D. A field test to evaluate physical performance capacity of association football players. *Sci. Football.* 3:9-11, 1990.
2. Bangsbo, J. Physiological demands. In: *Football (soccer).* B. Ekblom ed. Oxford: Blackwell Scientific Publications, 1994, pp. 43-59.
3. Bassett, F.A., and M. R. Boulay. Specificity of treadmill and cycle ergometer tests in triathletes, runners and cyclists. *Eur. J. App. Physiol.* 80:214-221, 2000.
4. Brahler, C.J., and S. E. Blank. VersaClimbing elicits higher $\dot{V}O_{2max}$ than does treadmill running or rowing ergometry. *Med. Sci.Sports Exerc.* 27:249-254, 1995.
5. Ekblom, B. A field test for soccer players. *Sci. Football.* 1:13-15, 1989.
6. Ramsbottom R., J. Brewer, and C. Williams. A progressive shuttle run test to estimate maximal oxygen uptake. *Br. J. Sports Med.* 22:141-144, 1988.

7. Smekal, G., R. Pokan, S. P. von Duvillard, R. Baron, H. Tschan, and N. Bachl. Comparison of laboratory and "on-court" endurance testing in tennis. *J. Sports Sci.* 21:242-249, 2000.
8. Smith, T.B., W. G. Hopkins, and N. A. Taylor. Respiratory responses of elite oarsmen, former oarsmen, and highly trained non-rowers during rowing, cycling and running. *Eur. J. Appl. Physiol.* 69:44-49, 1994.
9. Strømme, S.B., F. Ingjer, and H. D. Meen. Assessment of maximal aerobic power in specifically trained athletes. *J. Appl. Physiol.* 42:833-837, 1977.
10. Åstrand, P.O., and K. Rodahl. *Textbook of Work Physiology*. New York, NY: McGraw-Hill, 1986, pp. 312-495.
11. Versteg, P.G. and G. J. Kippersluis. Automated systems for measurement of oxygen uptake during exercise testing. *Int. J. Sports Med.* 10:107-112, 1989.
12. Torvik, P.Ø. and J. Helgerud. The validity of the portable metabolic test system Cortex Metamax. In: *Science and Skiing II.* E. Müller, H. Schwameder, C. Raschner, S. Lindinger and E. Kornexl, eds. Hamburg: Verlag Dr. Kovac, 2001, pp. 641-654.
13. Helgerud, J., F. Ingjer, and S. B. Strømme. Sex differences in performance-matched marathon runners. *Eur. J. Appl. Physiol.* 61:433-439, 1990.
14. Bland, J.M., and D. G. Altman. Statistical method for assessing agreement between two methods of clinical measurement. *Lancet.* 1:307-310, 1986.
15. Bangsbo, J. Energy demands in competitive soccer. *J. Sports Sci.* 12:S5-12, 1994.
16. Reilly, T. and D. Ball. The net physiological cost of dribbling a soccer ball. *Res. Quart. Exerc. Sport.* 55:267-271, 1984.

17. Helgerud, J., L. C. Engen, U. Wisløff, and J. Hoff. Aerobic endurance training improves soccer performance. *Med. Sci. Sports Exerc.* In press, 2001.

18. Apor, P. Successful formulae for fitness training. In: *Science and Football.* T. Reilly, A. Lees, K. Davids and W.J. Murphy, eds. London: E & FN Spon, 1988, pp. 95-107.

19. Davies, J.A., J. Brewer, and D. Atkin. Pre-season physiological characteristics of English first and second division soccer players. *J. Sports Sci.* 10:541-547, 1992.

20. Nowacki, P.E., D. Y. Cai, C. Buhl, and U. Krummelbein. Biological performance of German soccer players (professionals and juniors) tested by special ergometry and treadmill methods. In: *Science and Football.* T. Reilly, A. Lees, K. Davids and W.J. Murphy, eds. London: E & FN Spon, 1988, pp. 145-157.

21. Reilly, T. Football. In: *Physiology of Sports.* T. Reilly, N. Secher, P. Snell and C. Williams, eds. London: E & FN Spon, 1990, pp. 374-425.

22. Wisløff, U., J. Helgerud, and J. Hoff. Strength and endurance of elite soccer players. *Med. Sci. Sports Exerc.* 3:462-467, 1998.

23. Wagner, P.D. Determinants of maximal oxygen transport and utilization. *Ann. Rev. Physiol.* 58:21-50, 1996.

Endurance Training Into the Next Millenium; Muscular Strength Training Effects on Aerobic Endurance Performance: A Review

Jan Hoff, PhD;[1,2] Jan Helgerud, PhD;[1,2] Ulrik Wisløff, PhD
Departments of Sport Sciences[1] and Physiology and Biomedical Engineering,[2] Norwegian University of Science and Technology, Trondheim, Norway

Review of the research literature reveals conclusive evidence that work economy (the ratio of work output to energy input) in aerobic endurance performance is enhanced by a maximal strength training regimen with emphasis on neural adaptation. This type of training uses high loads with few repetitions and maximal mobilization of force in the concentric part of a movement. The highest training response seems to be in the rate of force development, but peak force and one repetition maximum also show significant changes. One repetition maximum improvement alone seems not to have a similar effect, which at least partially explains the differences in findings from previous research. Improved work economy may be due to increased power production and a shift in the power-load and load-velocity relationships. Further research is needed to determine whether this alters vascular blood flow and thus adds a circulatory component to the power component discussed here.
(Am J Med Sports. 2002;4:58–67)

Address for correspondence/reprint requests: Jan Hoff, PhD, Norwegian University of Science and Technology, Department of Physiology and Biomedical Engineering, Medical Faculty, N-7489 Trondheim, Norway
Manuscript received November 5, 1999; accepted March 27, 2000

While the effects of endurance training and strength training have been separately subjected to intensive research, the effect of combined endurance and strength training on endurance performance is sparsely documented.[1–6] Adaptation to exercise is considered to be primarily dependent on the specific type of training performed. The principle for maximal strength training is the use of high intensity, heavy resistance, and few repetitions to increase strength by hypertrophy of the muscle or by neural adaptation.[7,8] Endurance training, on the other hand, is based on movements performed with a high number of repetitions and light resistance. Several studies performed in the 1980s indicated that the combination of strength and endurance training resulted in an inhibition of the optimal strength development that would have occurred if strength training had been performed alone.[3,9] This review is focused on the mechanisms of strength and endurance performance and on how maximum strength training might alter endurance performance, as shown in some studies[2,10,11] but not in others.[12,13]

Endurance Performance

Endurance performance, as in long distance running or cross country skiing, imposes great demands on both the cardiovascular system and the employed locomotor organs. An efficient oxygen transport system is therefore vital. Endurance sports are demanding in terms of aerobic power, but performance is also influenced by somatic factors (e.g., gender, age, and body dimensions), psychological factors (e.g., attitude and motivation), environment (e.g., altitude and temperature), and probably primarily by training adaptation.[14,15] Endurance sports are favored by a predominance of slow-twitch (type 1) muscle fibers. Endurance performance is dependent upon the ability to supply the active muscle cells with adequate amounts of oxygen and essential nutrients, while eliminating heat, carbon dioxide, and other waste products and sustaining homeostasis in other parts of the body. When exercising, humans must transport oxygen from ambient air, down the respiratory passage to the lungs, through the cardiovascular system, and into the muscle cells. In turn, carbon dioxide must be transported from the muscle cell to ambient air. Therefore, there are several steps at which the oxygen transport pathway may be limited.

FACTORS DETERMINING MAXIMAL OXYGEN UPTAKE. DiPrampero and Ferretti[16] presented an integrated model that is based on electrical analogs of the O_2 pathway and uses drops in Po_2 to assign relative pathway impedance. The principal limitation with this approach is that the pressure drop from alveolar gas to arterial blood reflects the ratio of diffusive to perfusive conductance in the lung and not alveolar gas/blood diffusive resistance alone.[17] Thus, the pressure drop is determined not only by the lungs' ability to exchange O_2 but also by circulatory properties, such as blood flow and hemoglobin concentration. The same limitation applies to exchange within the muscles.

Wagner[18,19] devised an alternative approach. A numerical analysis interactively linking the lungs, circulation, and muscles was designed to compare the influences of each conductance component on maximal oxygen uptake (Vo_{2max}). It is represented by three equations: one describes mass balance for O_2 exchange between alveolar gas and pulmonary capillary blood, one describes diffuse uptake of O_2 in the lung capillaries, and one describes unloading of O_2 from the muscle capillaries. The conductances in question are alveolar ventilation (VE), cardiac output (Q), pulmonary diffusion capacity (DLO_2), and muscle diffusion capacity (DMO_2). Two other independent transport variables considered are hemoglobin concentration ([Hb]) and fraction of inspired O_2. For more details see Wagner.[19]

At maximal exercise, the majority of evidence points to a Vo_{2max} that is limited by O_2 availability.[20-23] However, in completely sedentary individuals Roca et al.[24] were not able to increase Vo_{2max} by making more O_2 available (hyperoxia). When Vo_{2max} is limited by the O_2 supply, it is generally thought that Q is primarily responsible, but at sea level, Hb, DLO_2, and DMO_2 have been found to be just as influential. Wagner[19] reported that with increasing altitude, the influence of Q and Hb fell, while that of VE, DLO_2, and DMO_2 progressively increased. At extreme altitude (PB=253 torr, equivalent to that at the summit of Mt. Everest), Vo_{2max} was independent of Q and Hb. However, pulmonary and muscle O_2 diffusive conductances are predicted to be of considerable influence on Vo_{2max} from sea level to the Everest summit.

In summary, at sea level, the critical convective and diffusive components of O_2 transport have evolved to optimal values. Thus, further increases have little effect on Vo_{2max}; however, with relatively little reserve the system is vulnerable to their reduction. At altitude, muscle diffusing capacity becomes the most important factor affecting Vo_{2max}.[18]

PHYSIOLOGIC DETERMINANTS OF CARDIORESPIRATORY ENDURANCE. Cardiorespiratory endurance has long been recognized as one of the fundamental components of physical fitness and performance in endurance events. Since accumulation of lactic acid is associated with skeletal muscle fatigue, anaerobic metabolism cannot contribute at a quantitatively significant level to the energy expended in endurance events, such as long distance running or cross country skiing. Therefore, during these types of events, maximal steady-rate Vo_2 functions as the primary determinant of the maximal work rate. Pate and Kriska[25] described a model that incorporates the three major factors that account for interindividual variance in aerobic endurance performance: Vo_{2max}, anaerobic threshold (Th_{an}), and work economy (C). Numerous published studies support this model.[26-30] Thus, the model should serve as a useful framework for comprehensive study of the effects of strength training on endurance performance.

Endurance is defined as the organism's ability to work at a relatively high intensity for a long time.[32] Endurance training, then, stresses the factors that allow exercise at moderate to high intensity for extended periods of time.[32] Vo_{2max} is probably the single most important factor determining success in an extreme aerobic endurance sport.[14] However, within the same person Vo_{2max} changes with different activities. Therefore, in order to obtain relevant values, emphasis is placed on testing in sport-specific activities. Testing competitive racers in cross country skiing shows that they have obtained higher VO_{2max} in skiing compared to treadmill running.[33] Therefore, special ergometers have been made to simulate cross country skiing in the laboratory.[34-36] In cross country skiing the demand of VO_{2max} is large: 85%–99% of the energy metabolism is due to aerobic processes.[34,37] The best international male cross country skiers, like the best middle and long distance runners, have Vo_{2max} of more than 80 $mL \cdot kg^{-1} \cdot min^{-1}$.[37,38] It has been well documented that mitochondrial density, oxidative enzyme activity, and capillary density increase with endurance training.[14]

Th_{an} determines the fraction of the maximal aerobic power that may be sustained for an extended period of time.[25] The Th_{an} was defined by Davis[39] as the intensity of work or Vo_2 at which the blood lactate concentration gradually starts to increase during continuous exercise. The blood lactate level ($[la^-]_b$) represents a balance between lactate production and removal, and there are individual patterns in these kinetics.[40] Lactate is not wasted. Without any loss of energy, the process of pyruvate transformation to lactate can be reversed. Pyruvate can thus be oxidized or to a smaller extent be a substrate for synthesis of glucose and glycogen. When oxidized it yields the remaining 92% of energy. Both resting and submaximally working skeletal muscle, as well as heart muscle and kidney cortex, can use lactate as a substrate.[14] The Th_{an} concept is appealing because it may be more sensitive to training-induced adaptations than is Vo_{2max} alone. Values as high as 90% of Vo_{2max} have been observed in some highly proficient endurance athletes.[41] Th_{an} changes with alteration in Vo_{2max}, but in terms of the percentage of Vo_{2max} the adaptability seems to be within a 10% range. The factors determining Th_{an} are not well known. However, muscle fiber type distribution, the potential for fat metabolism, and skeletal muscle lactic dehydrogenase isoenzyme distribution may be important determinants.[25]

Work economy, or C, is defined as the ratio of work output to oxygen cost. Conley and Krahenbuhl[28] and Helgerud[42] have shown intraindividual variations in gross oxygen cost during activity at a standard running velocity. The causes of this variability are not well understood, but it seems likely that anatomical features, mechanical skill, neuromuscular skill, and storage of elastic energy are important.[25] Running economy (C_R) is commonly defined as the steady-state Vo_2 in $mL \cdot kg^{-1} \cdot m^{-1}$ at a standard velocity,[28,41] or as the energy cost of running per meter ($mL \cdot kg^{-1} \cdot m^{-1}$).[29,42] Similarly, for upper body work in cross country skiers, double the poling work economy (C_{dp}) is expressed as oxygen cost per meter of double poling at submaximal work loads.[35,36]

Strength Training

Muscular strength and power are central qualities in sports performance. A variety of training methods are applied in an effort to increase strength and power, mostly in sports demanding acceleration and explosive force development, such as sprinting, jumping, and throwing. Strength is defined as the integrated result of several force-producing muscles performing maximally, either isometrically or dynamically, during a single voluntary effort in a defined task. Typically, maximal strength is defined in terms of one repetition maximum (1RM) in a standardized movement, as in the squat exercise. Power is the product of force and the inverse of time, i.e., it is the ability to produce as much force as possible in the shortest possible time. Results of research within the strength training area are equivocal, often because of differences in measurement techniques. Traditionally, much research has been conducted using isometric measures or isokinetic movements. Both of these techniques have limited interest in terms of prediction value for dynamic sports or everyday movements.

Muscles' ability to develop force is dependent on many different factors, of which the most common are initial position, speed of lengthening, speed of shortening, eccentric initial phase, types of muscle fibers, number of motor units active at the same time, cross-sectional area of the muscle, impulse frequency, and substrate availability for the muscle exercise.[43]

The classic force-velocity curve shows that the maximal force in a concentric activity is less than in an isometric contraction. The highest power is attained when the velocity of contraction is 25%–30% of the maximal value, at which point the force is about 30% of the maximal isometric strength,[44] although few strength training studies have been conducted on the basis of this conclusion. Kaneko et al.[45] found significant change in the force-velocity curve and corresponding improvement in mechanical power output as a result of muscle power training. However, their measurements were not made for more than 60% of maximal isometric strength. The development of training methods has traditionally been based upon specificity principles, and training is supposed to be sport-specific in terms of contraction type, contraction force, movements, and velocity.[7,43] Principally, two different mechanisms, muscular hypertrophy and neural adaptation, may cause development of muscular strength.

MUSCULAR HYPERTROPHY. Muscular hypertrophy is obviously an effect of strength training, and there is a connection between the cross-sectional area of the muscle and its potential for force development.[8] This increase is associated with a large increase in the myofibril content of the fibers.[46] During systematic strength training over a period of time, hypertrophy will occur in all muscle fiber types. However, several studies have shown that the fast-twitch fibers exhibit the greatest hypertrophy.[8,47]

In certain sports, increased body weight due to hypertrophy is not desirable because the athlete will have to transport a higher body mass. In addition, increased muscle mass does not necessarily increase the high velocity strength. Tesch and Larson[48] reported an impaired ability to develop torque at high velocity in body builders, in comparison to a reference group of competitive weight lifters. The decreased maximal speed of contraction results in a greater decrease in force at high velocities of the force-velocity curve. Although changes in the ability to develop torque at high velocities may be a consequence of the altered architecture of hypertrophied muscle, they may be related to velocity specificity. Typically, body builder training practices include a great volume of high resistance-slow velocity movement to promote the hypertrophic effect.[48]

Several methods for developing muscular hypertrophy have been reported.[49] Eight to 12 repetitions with submaximal resistance (60%–90% of maximal dynamic strength) in series are often used. The execution of the exercises changes from slow to fast, and the eccentric phase is particularly slow. One goal of this training is to totally exhaust the muscles. Microruptures might have an anabolic effect.[48] An increase in capillary density during training for hypertrophy is also reported,[49] and long-term training for hypertrophy has been shown to increase body weight.

NEURAL ADAPTATION. In recent years the focus of strength training has turned to neural adaptation.[43] The term "neural adaptation" is a broad description involving a number of factors, such as selective activation of motor units, synchronization, selective activation of muscles, ballistic contractions, increased rate coding (frequency), increased reflex potential, increased recruitment of motor units, and increased co-contractions of antagonists.[50] A notable part of the improvement in the ability to lift weights is due to an increased ability to coordinate other muscle groups involved in the movement, such as those that stabilize the body.[51]

To develop maximal force a muscle is dependent on as many active motor units as possible. In a maximal voluntary contraction the small oxidative fibers are recruited first[52] and the fastest glycolytic fibers are recruited last in the hierarchy. At early stages of a training period an increase in activity of fast glycolytic fibers is seen with an increase in strength.[7] The central nervous system recruits motor units by sending nerve impulses to the motor neuron. The increased rate coding contributes to increased potential for force development.[7] An increased activation of the muscle may be due to a lower threshold of recruitment and an increased rate coding. These changes are possible explanations for increased strength.

Behm and Sale[43] suggest two major principles for maximal neural adaptation. To train the fastest motor units, which develop the highest force, one has to work against high loads (85%–95% of 1RM), which guarantees maximal voluntary contraction. Maximal advantage would be gained if the movements were trained with a rapid action, in addition to the high resistance. As a method to increase the rate of force development upon neural adaptation, Schmidtbleicher[8] suggests dynamic movements with a few repetitions (three to seven). The resistance should range from submaximal to maximal (85%–100% of 1RM), with explosive movements. This may give rise to neuromuscular adaptation with minimal hypertrophy.[53]

Long-term training studies have shown faster mobilization of nerve activity after intensive high-resistance training.[54,55] Among possible mechanisms for this are faster recruitment of motor units, and a faster firing rate in trained athletes. The normal firing frequency is approximately 10–60 Hz. An increase in the firing rate to 100 Hz may result in a faster recruitment of the muscle fibers, and therefore a possibly shorter time for maximal strength to develop.[8]

Much research (e.g., that of Behm and Sale[43]) has documented the existence of some velocity-specific effects of resistance training, though the mechanisms underlying these effects have not been clearly established. It has been suggested that the intent to make a high-speed contraction may be the most crucial factor in velocity specificity.[50] Also, findings by Almåsbakk and Hoff[53] point to the development of coordination as the determining factor in early velocity-specific strength gains. In addition, Sale[7] suggested that training exercises should simulate the sport movements as closely as possible in terms of movement pattern.

Jones and Rutherford[56] have shown an experimental gain in 1RM of 200%, followed by only 5%—barely significant—hypertrophy. Hoff and Almåsbakk[57] showed a 1RM gain of 35% in well trained subjects without changes in body weight or size of the muscle, indicating that neural adaptation also occurs subsequent to the early stages of strength training.

TRAINING STRENGTH. McDonagh and Davies[58] reviewed and summarized 11 research reports involving loads and repetitions. They stated that loads lower than 66% of 1RM conferred no increase in strength, even if up to 150 contractions per day were used, while loads higher than 66% of 1RM increased maximal voluntary contraction from 0.2% to 2% per day. Moreover, loads higher than 66% with as few as 10 repetitions per day produced a significant increase in strength. The increases in dynamic strength were greatest when the heavier loads were used. Dons et al.[59] showed that a load of 80% of 1RM gave a significant increase in 1RM, while a load of 50% of 1RM did not, even if both groups performed the same mechanical work each day.

Training adaptations seem to be different for neural adaptation and for hypertrophy. Training for hypertrophy should emphasize eccentric/concentric actions with high loads, but with a number of repetitions higher than six.[48,49] Muscular damage may trigger hypertrophy and is the rationale behind the suggested practice in body building, in which 10–12 repetitions are used; the last one or two repetitions are forced, such that the subject cannot perform but tries and performs only with necessary assistance. Body builders typically use short pauses (1–2 minutes) and a minimum of four to five sets to generate a complete exhaustion of the muscle group.

For neural adaptation, and hence explosive training, it is important to stress all motor units, but especially the high threshold, fast-twitch motor units. Nardone et al.[60] have shown that, unlike Henneman's size principle of orderly recruitment of motor units, some high threshold, fast-twitch motor units fire prior to the slow-twitch, low threshold motor units with eccentric training. This points toward training that includes both eccentric and concentric contractions. For increases in rate of force development, even higher forces with a lower number of repetitions is recommended. Adaptations resulting from this high intensity training seem to be rapid recruitment of motor units and an increased firing rate of motoneurones, compared to neural activity in untrained people.[55,61,62] The number of sets in maximum strength or rate of force development training is often three to five, so that one exercise in a training session typically includes 20 repetitions.[8] If the goal is to increase the rate of force development and maximal strength from neural adaptation without changes in body weight, a training regimen of five to six repetitions in three to four series using maximal mobilization of force, or maximal "intended" velocity, in the concentric phase is recommended.[8,43,53,56,57]

Dimensional Scaling

Comparisons of Vo_{2max} using the traditional expression $mL \cdot kg^{-1} \cdot min^{-1}$ are both very routine and functionally imprecise. As has been suggested by von Döbeln as early as 1956,[14] Vo_2 is a measure of power and, in order to be mass-independent, should be expressed in mL per kg lean body mass raised to a power of 2/3. Results from Bergh et al.[37] and Helgerud[42] support the suggestion that neither submaximal Vo_2 nor Vo_{2max} increases in proportion to body mass during running. For running, it was concluded that it would be better to express Vo_2 in the units $mL \cdot kg^{-0.75} \cdot min^{-1}$ to evaluate the capacity of the oxygen transport system. These data agree with the reduced exponent predicted from the theory of similarity or dimensional scaling.[14] In this way, the effect of body dimensions on several performances and/or capacity measures can be calculated. This ought to be considered when comparing individuals or groups with different body mass (i.e., children with adults or males with females). Heavy athletes will be underestimated using the traditional Vo_{2max} expression $mL \cdot kg^{-1} \cdot min^{-1}$, and lighter athletes, such as endurance athletes, will be overestimated. When evaluating work economy at submaximal exercise the opposite is true, i.e., the heavier subject will be overestimated and the lighter underestimated.

Dimensional scaling must also be considered when evaluating strength measures.[64] In two geometrically similar and quantitatively identical individuals, one may expect all linear dimensions (L) to be proportional. The length of the arms, the legs, and the individual muscles will have a ratio L:1, the cross section area L^2:1, and the volume ratio L^3:1. Since muscular strength is related to muscle cross-sectional area, and body mass (m_b) varies directly with body volume, whole-body muscular strength measures will vary in proportion to $m_b^{0.67}$. In practical terms this means that strength training goals should not be determined in relation to body mass. A training goal of 0.8 times body weight for bench presses or 1.5 times body weight for half squats is easy for the light individual, but very difficult for the large one. Relative strength should thus be compared between individuals in terms of $kg \cdot m_b^{-0.67}$.

Strength Training Effects on Endurance Performance

The effect of combined strength and endurance training on physical performance has been a popular research topic in the last decade. It has been concluded in several studies[3,9,12,65,66] that endurance training inhibits or interferes with strength development. Few studies, however, have examined the impact of strength training on endurance performance. Hickson et al.[2] reported a 27% increase in parallel squat 1RM after 10 weeks of maximal strength training using squats and three supplementary exercises. Vo_{2max} was unchanged during the same period, while short-term endurance (4–8 minutes), measured as time to exhaustion during treadmill running and on a bicycle ergometer, increased by 13% and 11%, respectively. Mean Vo_{2max} was 54.5 and 60.2 $mL \cdot kg^{-1} \cdot min^{-1}$, as tested in cycling and running, respectively. Vo_{2max} and peak oxygen uptake (Vo_{2peak}) achieved during a specific sport activity are the traditional determinants of endurance performance.[35,36,67] Other important factors, such as Th_{an} and C, should be included. Among individuals with similar Vo_{2max} and/or Vo_{2peak}, work economy and performance can vary considerably.[42,68]

Nakao et al.[69] found no effects on Vo_{2max} after introducing maximal strength training to a group of students with an initial Vo_{2max} level ranging from 53.4–60.0 $mL \cdot kg^{-1} \cdot min^{-1}$ over a 3-year period.

Johnston et al.[10] carried out a 10-week strength intervention study in which six female subjects classified as "distance runners" trained with 14 different strength exercises; another six subjects served as controls and performed only endurance training. During the intervention period, 1RM parallel squats changed from 58.3 kg to 81.8 kg. The initial mean Vo_{2max} was 50.5 $mL \cdot kg^{-1} \cdot min^{-1}$, or 2.84 $L \cdot min^{-1}$. Vo_{2max} was unchanged during the intervention period, but running economy, expressed as $mL \cdot kg^{-1} \cdot m^{-1}$, improved significantly; however, no performance test was carried out. Their study design has two principal problems. First, since so many different strength training exercises with different loads and repetitions were imposed at the same time, it is difficult if not impossible to determine mechanisms for the training adaptations. Secondly, the experimental group gained weight at an average of 1.3 kg in the 10-week training period, probably from the "body building"-like portion of the training regimen. As stated in the theoretical introduction, weight gain will result in overestimation of improvements in running economy expressed as $mL \cdot kg^{-1} \cdot m^{-1}$.[37,42] There was no difference in oxygen uptake between the two groups at the two velocities tested, 2.36 $L \cdot min^{-1}$ vs. 2.32 $L \cdot min^{-1}$ and 2.52 $L \cdot min^{-1}$ vs. 2.49 $L \cdot min^{-1}$. Thus, the difference between the groups in calculated work economy must have been due to weight gain in the training group. Recalculating the running economy using the weight-neutral expression $mL \cdot kg^{-0.75} \cdot m^{-1}$ reduces the intervention-induced improvement in running economy, probably to a nonsignificant level.

Paavolainen et al.[70] conducted a 9-week explosive strength training intervention in a group of cross country skiers. They replaced 32% of endurance training time in the experimental group (n=12) and 3% in the control group (n=10) with 30–200 contractions per training session and 5–20 repetitions per set, using light loads and high intensity in a variety of jumping exercises and sprints. They found no changes in maximal isometric strength, but a group-by-time interaction showed a significant difference from the control group as the control group reduced their strength. At the same time, Vo_{2max} changed in the experimental group from 67.7 to 70.2 $mL \cdot kg^{-1} \cdot min^{-1}$. Improvement in a 5-km run was shown as a group-by-training interaction, but since the control group was one half minute slower than the experimental group and both groups were exposed to a similar training regimen in the intervention period, a correct interpretation is difficult. The experimental group showed improvement in running economy expressed as $mL \cdot kg^{-1} \cdot m^{-1}$ at a standard velocity. As changes occurred both in Vo_{2max} and in body weight (1.2 kg between groups) from pre- to post-test, there is a question of how much of the reduced oxygen cost per meter was caused by running economy improvements. Nevertheless, along with other studies, this seems to be an indication that power enhancement might improve work economy. In line with several other experiments in this type of research, an intervention consisting of different training regimens in the same experimental group makes it very difficult to trace physiologic mechanisms underlying the changes in dependent variables.

Bishop et al.[13] conducted a 12-week maximal strength training intervention in a group of female cyclists (n=14) with a Vo_{2max} of 48[2] (SD, 5.8). The strength intervention was carried out twice a week using a resistance machine and three different training protocols, ranging from 50%–80% of 1RM and from 15–5 repetitions, respectively. 1RM in squat strength on the resistance machine increased by 35.9%, and body weight increased in the experimental group by 0.9 kg, but no changes were observed in any of the dependent variables Vo_{2peak}, Th_{an}, or performance in a 1-hour cycling test. The authors' conclusion is that factors other than the increase in leg strength per se may be responsible for the previously reported improvements after resistance training.

A variable that complicates evaluation of the impact of strength training on endurance performance is the training status of the subjects investigated. The majority of studies investigating strength and endurance training interactions have examined sedentary or moderately active subjects, using strength training regimens with low resistance and a high number of repetitions.[71–73] When subjects are initially untrained, the effects of this type of strength training on endurance performance can be substantial and may operate via mechanisms that are similar to those observed in endurance training.[71,74] However, in well trained, specifically adapted athletes, auxiliary strength training methods may fail to improve endurance performance[42,75] and may even inhibit performance if they are conducted at the expense of specific training volume. They may also require greater task specificity to achieve continued improvement,[51,62] although one study[57] showed substantial strength improvement in a non-task-specific exercise in trained athletes, with a carryover effect to performance.

If the training regimen used by Behm and Sale,[43] Hoff and Almåsbakk,[57] and Almåsbakk and Hoff[53] proved effective on the basis of coordination rather than muscle hypertrophy, the argument that strength training increases body weight and thereby might impair endurance performance[2,49,76] might not be a valid one. In a series of experiments at our laboratory we hypothesized that maximal strength training with emphasis on mobilization in the concentric part of the movement will enhance endurance performance even in well trained endurance athletes.

Helgerud et al.[77] conducted an 8-week maximal strength training intervention study using well trained cross country skiers (Vo_{2max}, 69.7 $mL \cdot kg^{-1} \cdot min^{-1}$; SD, 2.2) double poling on a well tested ergometer[35,36] (Figure 1). Maximal strength training consisted of three sets of five repetitions, using high loads and emphasizing maximal mobilization of force, three times a week using a cable pulley (Figure 2). Total training for the group was 9.1 hours per $week^{-1}$, and the strength training intervention was 0.45 hours per week. 1RM in double poling improved significantly from 40.3 kg to 44.4 kg in the experimental group. Peak force at a standardized workload of 80% of 1RM was improved by 34%, and time to peak force showed improvements of 50% and 60% for the 80% and 60% 1RM loads, respectively. No changes occurred in Vo_{2max} or Vo_{2peak}. Time to exhaustion at maximal aerobic velocity improved from 6.49 minutes to 10.18 minutes (significant relative to the control group). C at a double poling velocity of 181 m·sec^{-1} changed from 1.02 to 0.74 mL•kg$^{-0.67}$•m^{-1} and there was no change in body weight. These findings support those of Hickson et al.[2] and Paavolainen et al.,[70] indicating that change in aerobic endurance performance, as a result of change in power or rate of force development, occurs through an improved C, not through changes in Vo_{2max}.

Hoff et al.[11] repeated the above-mentioned experiment using trained female cross country skiers (n=15; Vo_{2max}=55.3 mL•kg^{-1}•min^{-1}). Since Th_{an} was not measured in the previous experiment, the hypothesis in this study was that a maximal strength training regimen with emphasis on mobilization of force would result in improved C and Th_{an}; furthermore, C would improve by a reduction in relative workload (% 1RM) and time to peak force during double poling.

Figure 1. The double poling ski ergometer

Figure 2. Cable pulley maximal strength training with emphasis on mobilization of force

1RM increased by 14.5% and double poling C (C_{dp}) was reduced from 1.42 to 1.10 mL•kg$^{-0.67}$•m^{-1}. At maximal aerobic velocity, time to exhaustion changed from 5.2 to 12.3 minutes in the experimental group; time to peak force was reduced from 370 to 270 msec; and no change occurred in double poling frequency. Time to peak force at 80% 1RM changed from 370 to 260 msec. No changes occurred in Vo_{2max}, Th_{an}, or in body weight. It was concluded that maximal strength training with emphasis on mobilization improves aerobic endurance performance through improved work economy, without changes in Vo_{2max} or Th_{an}. The improvement in work economy is probably due to an improved rate of force development, and thus of power production, and to a smaller extent due to the relatively smaller fraction of 1RM employed, as previous research has demonstrated no such connection.[69]

A third experiment in this series was carried out by Østerås et al.,[78] who studied highly trained male cross country skiers (n=19; Vo_{2max} >65.0 mL•kg^{-1}•min^{-1}) in a 9-week maximal strength training intervention for upper body and double poling, with emphasis on maximal mobilization of force. The hypothesis was that an increased 1RM, and most importantly an increased rate of force development, will improve C_{dp} and that this mechanism is due to increased power production and a shift in the power-load and load-velocity relationships. 1RM increased from 43.8 kg to 53.4 kg, and relative strength (1RM•$m_b^{-0.67}$) increased from 2.37 kg to 2.88 kg. Time to exhaustion on maximal aerobic velocity changed from 5.26 minutes to 8.47 minutes. No changes occurred in body weight, Vo_{2max}, Vo_{2peak}, or Th_{an}. C_{dp} changed from 1.13 to 1.03 mL•kg$^{-0.67}$•m^{-1}. Total training was 14.7 hours·week^{-1}; the strength training regimen of three series of six repetitions employed only 45 minutes of this time. A shift in the power-load and load-velocity relationships to the right is shown in Figure 3. Peak force employed at maximal aerobic velocity in double poling was equivalent to 25.9% and 21.1% of the peak force in the dynamic execution of 1RM developed on the modified cable pulley at pre- and post-test, respectively. Power production was enhanced at all loads higher than 10% of maximal voluntary contraction. In line with previous studies, improved rates of force development and power production with a maximal strength training regimen that emphasized mobilization of force improved C_{dp}. The changes in C_{dp} were correlated with a shift in the power-load and load-velocity relationships.

The last three experiments described involved

use of upper body muscles, which normally are much less trained and of a smaller volume than weight-bearing muscles, as also indicated by the fact that their Vo_{2peak} is 85%–90% of Vo_{2max} during running.

Hoff carried out an experiment similar to the previous studies (Hoff J, unpublished data), to determine whether maximal strength squat training using high loads, few repetitions, and maximal mobilization of force might improve running economy, as has been shown with work economy in the upper body in previous research. Twenty-four trained subjects from three soccer teams, with a mean Vo_{2max} of 4.36 L, 59.8 $mL \cdot kg^{-1} \cdot min^{-1}$, or 174.5 $mL \cdot kg^{-0.75} \cdot min^{-1}$, participated in the study. The training group performed maximal strength training consisting of five repetitions in four series of loads higher than 85% of 1RM, with emphasis on maximal mobilization of force in the concentric action, three times per week for 8 weeks. The control group engaged in technical soccer training for the same amount of time. In the training group, 1RM increased by 33.7%, from 161.3 kg to 215.6 kg in half squats, with no change in body weight. No change occurred in the control group. Rate of force development at maximal voluntary contraction improved by 52.3% and peak force improved by 9.6% in the training group, while no change was observed in the control group. Running economy improved by 4.7%, from 0.788 to 0.751 $mL \cdot kg^{-0.75} \cdot m^{-1}$, while no change was observed in the controls. No change was observed in the parameters Vo_{2max} and Th_{an}.

Like upper body work economy, C_R seems to be improved with maximal strength training with emphasis on fast mobilization of force. The improvement in C_R seems, however, to be smaller in the larger, weight-bearing leg and hip muscles. This might be due to the fact that they are initially better trained due to daily use. As shown in Figure 3, the improvements are also higher in the load-velocity and power-load relationships as the load becomes higher. For the power-load relationship, that extends to a load approximately 40% of 1RM.

Conclusions

From the research carried out to date, there is conclusive evidence that work economy in endurance performance is enhanced by a maximal strength training regimen with emphasis on neural adaptations. This type of training primarily enhances rate of force development but also, to a certain extent, peak force and 1RM. It seems that a change in 1RM alone does not have the same effect. An alternative training regimen that increases body weight does not have an effect on rate of force development. This is in line with the lack of effect of 1RM improvement on high velocity movements, as shown in strength training research, as these are dependent upon high velocity training conducted in the same period of time. At present, it is not known to what extent the improved work economy is load-dependent. The experiments conducted by Paavolainen[70] and by Almåsbakk and Hoff[53] indicate that similar rate of force developments as those that occur with the use of heavy loads might be possible. Maximal mobilization of force, however, seems to be a key factor in improving rate of force development and thus work economy. Maximal strength training with emphasis on mobilization also changes the power-load and load-velocity relationships, which seems to make a standardized workload relatively easier.

As the work frequency at maximal aerobic velocity does not change, but rate of force development and also, to a certain extent, peak force increase from this type of maximal strength training, it is logical that the improved performance could partly be explained by a longer muscle relaxation period. Although the force developed in each contraction may be only a fraction of the peak force, the arterial inflow occurs almost exclusively between contractions.[79] A linear coupling exists between blood flow and mechanical work or oxygen uptake at the muscle level.[80,81] The improved rate of force development might therefore reduce blood flow during muscle contraction with a standard workload, since VO_2 is reduced, due to improved work economy. This is a line of future research.

PRACTICAL APPLICATIONS. Improved work economy is as important to everyday life and quality of life as it is to athletes' performance. Increased strength and ability to mobilize force make all kinds of movements using the same muscles easier, whether it is walking the hills, playing golf, or car-

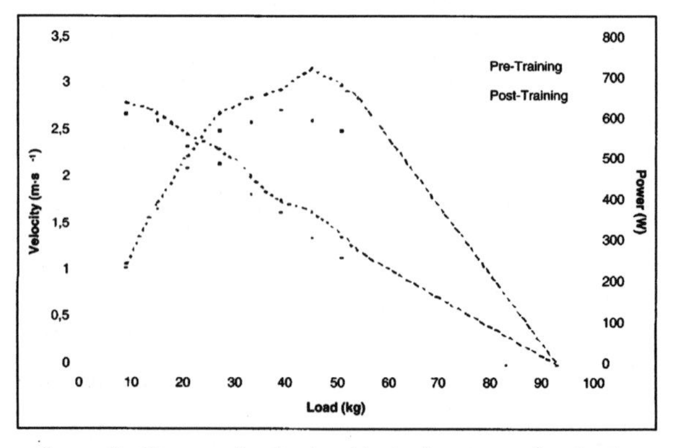

Figure 3. Changes in the load/velocity-power/load relationship after maximal strength training with emphasis on fast mobilization of force (mean and SD)

rying out heavy labor, such as lifting goods or carrying mail. Effective training for improvement in work economy involves high loads and few repetitions. Typically, a regimen of five repetitions in four series, with emphasis on maximal mobilization of force in the concentric part of the movement, such as in squats, improves walking and running economy. In primary care practice, the risk of injury might be considered if free weights are used, and safer training equipment might be recommended, such as a hack-lift, squat apparatus, or seated leg press. There is, however, evidence that the transfer to regular motion might be somewhat less than when using free weights. Maximal mobilization of force after a short stop when the load has been lowered is important. Also, in elderly people, positive effects are seen in clinic after four series of five repetitions of seated leg presses, with emphasis on fast mobilization of force, carried out three times per week. ■

REFERENCES

1 Hickson RC, Rosenkoetter MA, Brown MM. Strength training effects on aerobic power and short term endurance. *Med Sci Sports Exerc.* 1980;12(5):336–339.
2 Hickson RC, Dvorak BA, Gorostiaga EM, et al. Potential for strength and endurance training to amplify endurance performance. *J Appl Physiol.* 1988;65: 2285–2290.
3 Dudley GA, Djamil R. Incompatibility of endurance- and strength-training modes of exercise. *J Appl Physiol.* 1985;59:1446–1451.
4 Hunter G, Demment R, Miller D. Development of strength and maximal oxygen uptake during simultaneous training for strength and endurance. *J Sports Med.* 1987;27(32):269–275.
5 Chromiak JA, Mulvaney DR. A review: the effects of combined strength and endurance training on strength development. *J Appl Physiol.* 1990;4:55–60.
6 Tanaka H, Swensen T. Impact of resistance training on endurance performance. *Sports Med.* 1998;25 (3):191–200.
7 Sale DG. Neural adaptations in strength training. In: Komi PV, ed. *Strength and Power in Sport.* London, UK: Blackwell Scientific Publications; 1992:249–295.
8 Schmidtbleicher D. Training for power event. In: Komi PV, ed. *Strength and Power in Sport.* London, UK: Blackwell Scientific Publications; 1992:381–395.
9 Hickson RC. Interference of strength development by simultanious training for strength and endurance. *Eur J Appl Physiol.* 1980;45:255–263.
10 Johnston RE, Quinn TJ, Kertzer R, et al. Strength training in female distance runners: impact on running economy. *J Strength Conditioning Res.* 1997;11(4): 224–229.
11 Hoff J, Helgerud J, Wisløff U. Maximal strength training improves work economy in trained female cross-country skiers. *Med Sci Sports Exerc.* 1999;31(6):870–877.
12 Kraemer WJ, Patton JF, Gordon SE, et al. Compatibility of high-intensity strength and endurance training on hormonal and skeletal muscle adaptations. *J Appl Physiol.* 1995;73:976–989.
13 Bishop D, Jenkins DG, MacKinnon LT, et al. The effects of strength training on endurance performance and muscle characteristics. *Med Sci Sports Exerc.* 1999; 31(6):886–891.
14 Åstrand P-O, Rodahl K. *Textbook of Work Physiology.* New York, NY: McGraw-Hill Book Company; 1986.
15 Maughan RJ, Reilly T, Secher N, et al. Marathon running. In: Reilly T, et al., eds. *Physiology of Sports.* London, UK: E & FN Spon; 1969:121–152.
16 DiPrampero P, Ferretti G. Factors limiting maximal oxygen consumption in humans. *Respir Physiol.* 1990;80:113–128.
17 Piiper J, Scheid P. Model of capillary-alveolar equilibration with special reference to O_2 uptake in hypoxia. *Respir Physiol.* 1981;46:193–208.
18 Wagner PD. Algebraic analysis of the determinants of Vo_{2max}. *Respir Physiol.* 1993;93:221–237.
19 Wagner PD. A theoretical analysis of factors determining Vo_{2max} at sea level and altitude. *Respir Physiol.* 1996;106(3):329–343.
20 Powers SK, Laler J, Dempsey J, et al. Effects of incomplete pulmonary gas exchange on Vo_{2max}. *J Appl Physiol.* 1989;66:2491–2495.
21 Wagner PD. Central and peripheral aspects of oxygen transport and adaptations with exercise. *Sports Med.* 1991;11:133–142.
22 Knight DR, Schaffartzik W, Poole DC, et al. Effects of hyperoxia on maximal leg O_2 supply and utilization in humans. *J Appl Physiol.* 1993;75:2586–2594.
23 Richardson RS, Leigh JS, Wagner PD et al. Cellular PO_2 as a determinant of maximal mitochondrial O_2 consumption in trained human skeletal muscle. *J Appl Physiol.* 1999;87:321–331.
24 Roca J, Agustí AGN, Alonso A, et al. Effects of training on muscle O_2 transport at Vo_{2max}. *J Appl Physiol.* 1992;73:1067–1076.
25 Pate RR, Kriska A. Physiological basis of the sex difference in cardiorespiratory endurance. *Sports Med.* 1984;1:87–98.
26 Pollock ML. Submaximal and maximal working capacity of elite distance runners. Part 1: cardiorespiratory aspects. *Ann N Y Acad Sci.* 1977;301:310–322.
27 Farrell PA, Wilmore JH, Coyle EF, et al. Plasma lactate accumulation and distance running performance. *Med Sci Sports Exerc.* 1979;11:338–344.
28 Conley DL, Krahenbuhl GS. Running economy and distance running performance of highly trained athletes. *Med Sci Sports Exerc.* 1980;12:248–252.
29 DiPrampero PE, Atcho G, Brückner JC, et al. The energetics of endurance running. *Eur J Appl Physiol.* 1986;55:259–266.
30 Bunc V, Heller J. Energy cost of running in similarly trained men and women. *Eur J Appl Physiol.* 1989; 59:178–183.
31 Saltin B. Arbeidsfysiologi (exercise physiology). In: *Idrætsmedicin for almen praksis.* København Denmark: Lægeforeningens forlag; 1989:47–59.
32 Saltin B. Maximal oxygen uptake: limitations and maleability. In: Nazar K, Terjung, RL eds. *International Perspectives in Exercise Physiology.* Champaign, IL: Human Kinetics Publishers; 1990:26–40.
33 Strømme S, Ingjer F, Meen HD. Assesment of maximal aerobic power in specifically trained athletes. *J Appl Physiol.* 1977;42(6):833–837.
34 Mygind E, Larsson B, Klausen K. Evaluation of a specific test in cross-country-skiing. *J Sports Sci.* 1991;9: 249–257.
35 Wisløff U, Helgerud J. Evaluation of a new upper body ergometer for cross-country skiers. *Med Sci Sports Exerc.* 1998;30:1314–1320.
36 Wisløff U, Helgerud J. Methods for evaluating peak oxygen uptake and anaerobic threshold in upper body of cross-country skiers. *Med Sci Sports Exerc.* 1998; 30:963–970.
37 Bergh U, Sjødin B, Forsberg A, et al. The relationship between body mass and oxygen uptake during running in humans. *Med Sci Sports Exerc.* 1991;23:205–211.
38 Ingjer F. Maximal oxygen uptake as a predictor of performance ability in woman and man elite cross-country skiers. *Scand J Med Sports.* 1991;1:25–30.
39 Davis JA. Anaerobic threshold: review of the concepts and directions of future research. *Med Sci Sports Exerc.*

1985;17:6–18.
40 Brooks GA. Lactate production under fully aerobic conditions: the lactate shuttle during rest and exercise. *Fed Proc.* 1986;45:2924–2929.
41 Costill DL, Thomas H, Roberts E. Fractional utilization of the aerobic capacity during distance running. *Med Sci Sports Exerc.* 1973;5:248–252.
42 Helgerud J. Maximal oxygen uptake, anaerobic threshold and running economy in women and men with similar performances level in marathons. *Eur J Appl Physiol.* 1994;68:155–161.
43 Behm DG, Sale DG. Velocity specificity of resistance training. *Sports Med.* 1993;15(6):374–388.
44 Moritani T, Muro M, Ishida K, et al. Electromyographic analyses of the effects of muscle power training. *J Med Sport Sci (Jpn).* 1987;1:23–32.
45 Kaneko M, Fuchimoto T, Toji H, et al. Training effect on different loads on the force-velocity relationship and mechanical output in human muscle. *Scand J Sports Sci.* 1983;5:50–55.
46 Goldspink G. Cellular and molecular aspects of adaption in sceletal muscle. In: Komi PV, ed. *Strength and Power in Sport.* London, UK: Blackwell Scientific Publications; 1992:211–229.
47 McDougall JD. Hypertrophy or hyperplasia. In: Komi PV, ed. *Strength and Power in Sport.* London, UK: Blackwell Scientific Publications; 1992:3–6.
48 Tesch P, Larson L. Muscle hypertrophy in bodybuilders. *Eur J Appl Physiol.* 1982;49:301–306.
49 Tesch PA. Short- and long-term histochemical and biological adaptations in muscle. In: Komi PB, ed. *Strength and Power in Sport.* London, UK: Blackwell Scientific Publications; 1992:381–395.
50 Behm DG. Neuromuscular implications and applications of resistance training. *J Strength Conditioning Res.* 1995;4:264–274.
51 Rutherford OM, Jones A. The role of coordination in strength training. *Eur J Appl Physiol.* 1986;55:100–105.
52 Freund HJ. Motor unit and muscle activity in voluntary motor control. *Physiol Rev.* 1983;63:387.
53 Almåsbakk B, Hoff J. Coordination, the determinant of velocity specificity? *J Appl Physiol.* 1996;80(5): 2046–2052.
54 Moritani T, de Vries HA. Neural factors vs. hypertrophy in time course of muscle strength gain. *Am J Phys Med Rehab.* 1979;58:115–130.
55 Komi PV. Training of muscle strength and power: interaction of neuromotoric, hypertrophic and mechanical factors. *Int J Sports Med.* 1986;7(suppl):10–16.
56 Jones DA, Rutherford OM. Human muscle strength training: the effects of three different regimes and the nature of the resultant changes. *J Physiol.* 1987; 391:1–11.
57 Hoff J, Almåsbakk B. The effects of maximum strength training on throwing velocity and muscle strength in female team-handball players. *J Strength Conditioning Res.* 1995;9(4):255–258.
58 McDonagh MJN, Davies CTM. Adaptive response of mammalian skeletal muscle to exercise with high loads. *Eur J Appl Physiol.* 1984;52:139–155.
59 Dons B, Bollerup K, Bonde-Pedersen F, et al. The effect of weight-lifting exercise related to muscle fibre composition and muscle cross-sectional area in humans. *Eur J Appl Physiol.* 1979;40:95–106.
60 Nardone A, Romano C, Schieppati M. Selective recruitment of high threshold motor units during voluntary isotonic lengthening of active muscles. *J Physiol.* 1989;409:451–471.
61 Schmidtbleicher D, Bührle M. Neuronal adaptation and increase of cross-sectional area studying different strength training methods. In: Johnson S, ed. *Biomechanics XB.* Champaign, IL: Human Kinetics; 1987;615–620.
62 Häkkinen K, Alén M, Komi PV. Neuromuscular, anaerobic, and aerobic performance characteristics of elite power athletes. *Eur J Appl Physiol.* 1984;53:97–105.
63 Behm DG, Sale DG. Intended rather than actual movement velocity determines velocity-specific training response. *J Appl Physiol.* 1993;74:359–368.
64 Wisløff U, Helgerud J, Hoff J. Strength and endurance of elite soccer players. *Med Sci Sports Exerc.* 1998; 30(3):462–467.
65 Chromiac JA, Mulvaney DR. A review: the effects of combined strength and endurance training on strength development. *J Appl Sport Sci Res.* 1990;4(2):55–60.
66 Hennessy LC, Watson AWS. The interference effects of training for strength and endurance simultaneously. *J Strength Conditioning Res.* 1994;8(1):12–19.
67 Savard G, Kiens B, Saltin B. Central cardiovascular factors as limits to endurance; with a note on the distinction between maximal oxygen uptake and endurance fitness. In: MacLeod D, ed. *Exercise: Benefits, Limits and Adaptations.* London, UK: E & FN Spon; 1987:162–180.
68 Costill DL, Branam G, Eddy D, et al. Determinants of marathon running success. *Intern Zeitschr Angew Physiol.* 1971;29:249–254.
69 Nakao M, Inoue Y, Murakami H. Longitudinal study of the effect of high intensity weight training on aerobic capacity. *Eur J Appl Physiol.* 1994;70:20–25.
70 Paavolainen L, Häkkinen K, Hämäläinen I, et al. Explosive strength training improves 5-km running time by improving running economy and muscle power. *J Appl Physiol.* 1999;86(5):1527–1533.
71 Marcinik EJ, Pott J, Schlabach G, et al. Effects of strength training on lactate threshold and endurance performance. *Med Sci Sports Exerc.* 1991;23(6):739–743.
72 McCarty JP, Agre JC, Graf BK, et al. Compatibility of adaptive responses with combining strength and endurance training. *Med Sci Sports Exerc.* 1995;3:429–426.
73 Parker ND, Hunter GR, Treuth MS, et al. Effects of strength training on cardiovascular responses during a submaximal walk and a weight-loaded walking test in older females. *J Cardiopulm Res.* 1996;16:56–62.
74 Schantz PG, Kallman M. Strength training is ineffective for oxidative metabolism. *Swimming Tech.* 1989;5:5–6.
75 Bell GJ, Petersen SR, Quinney AH, et al. The effect of velocity-specific strength training on peak torque and anaerobic rowing power. *J Sport Sci.* 1989;7:205–214.
76 Nelson AG, Arnall DA, Loy SF, et al. Consequences of combining strength and endurance regimens. *Phys Ther.* 1990;70:287–294.
77 Helgerud J, Vik JT, Hoff J. The effect of maximal power training on endurance in the upper body in highly trained male cross-country skiers. *Corpus, Psyche et Sociatas.* In press.
78 Østerås H, Helgerud J, Hoff J. Maximal strength training effects on force-velocity and force-power relationship explain improvements in aerobic performance. *Corpus, Psyche et Sociatas.* In press.
79 Shoemaker JK, Hodge L, Hughson RL. Cardiorespiratory kinetics and femoral artery blood velocity during dynamic knee extension exercise. *J Appl Physiol.* 1994;77: 2625–2632.
80 Andersen P, Saltin B. Maximal perfusion of skeletal muscle in man. *J Physiol.* 1985;366:233–249.
81 Richardson RS, Poole DC, Knight DR, et al. High muscle bloodflow in man: is maximal O_2 extraction compromised? *J Appl Physiol.* 1993;75:1911–1916.

GENDER DIFFERENCES IN STRENGTH AND ENDURANCE OF ELITE SOCCER PLAYERS

J. Helgerud, U. Wisløff, J. Hoff
Norwegian University of Science and Technology, Department of Physiology and biomedical engineering.
N-7489 Trondheim, Norway

Introduction

During the last decade women soccer has become a popular event. Differences between male and female athletes are obviously not only genetic, but are also influenced by level of selection, training and competition.

Previous studies demonstrate a significant relationship between maximal oxygen uptake (VO_{2max}) and both distances covered during a game and number of sprints attempted by a player (Bangsbo 1991). Current research suggests that the female and male players tax the aerobic and anaerobic energy systems to a similar level. Much of the same proportions of the game appear to be devoted to exercise of varying intensities (Davis and Brewer 1993). During a game the average intensity is close to anaerobic threshold for both males and females (Davies and Brewer 1993, Reilly 1994a,). Women are however reported to cover a shorter distance (about 8.5km) than their male counterparts (about 10 km) during a game (Davis and Brewer 1993, Balsom 1994), probably based on differences in VO_{2max}.

The physical and physiological characteristics of female soccer players are comparable with those of other female game players and are more favourable than average for the population. VO_{2max} values of between 47 and 58 $ml \cdot kg^{-1} \cdot min^{-1}$ have been reported for elite female players (Davies and Brewer 1993). VO_{2max} for male players is normally reported between 55 and 65 ml · kg^{-1} · min^{-1} (Davis et al. 1992, Wisløff et al. 1998). After puberty, males have 10-15% higher blood hemoglobin concentration ([Hb]) than females. Cureton et al. (1986) concluded that the gender differences in [Hb] accounts for a significant, but small portion of the sex differences in VO_{2max}. When trying to distinguish biological differences from the behavioural ones, it is important to know the subject's physical activity background. In groups of equally trained men and women, differences in VO_{2max} and heart rate responses to exercise were less than in studies in which subjects are not equated on physical activity (Helgerud 1994).

As was suggested by von Döbeln (1956) oxygen uptake is a measure of power and, in order to be independent of absolute body mass, should be expressed in ml per kg lean body mass raised to a power of 2/3 or 0.67. This dimensional scaling approach was supported by Bergh et al. (1991) and Helgerud (1994) who found that VO_{2max} relative to body mass raised to the power of 0.75 was most indicative of performance capacity in running. This was later confirmed by Wisløff et al.(1998) on elite male soccer players. This ought to be considered when comparing groups with different body mass, children with adults or males with females.

Strength and power share importance with endurance in soccer. Maximal strength refers to the highest force that can be performed by the neuromuscular system during one maximum voluntary contraction (1RM). Women have 60-80% of men's leg strength, but only 50-60 % of men's upper limb strength (Åstrand and Rodahl 1986). Dimensional scaling must also be considered when evaluating strength measures. Since muscular strength is proportional to muscle cross-sectional area, whole body muscular strength measures will vary in proportion to body mass raised to the power of 0.67(Åstrand and Rodahl 1986, Wisløff et al 1998).

An increase in maximal strength is usually connected with an improvement in relative strength and therefore with improvement of power abilities. A significant relationship has been observed among males between 1RM and sprints (Bührle and Schmidtbleicher 1993, Hoff and Almåsbakk 1995). This maximal strength/power performance relationship is supported by vertical jump test results as well as in 30 meters sprint results on male subjects (Schmidtbleicher 1992). Vertical jump values are reported between 50 and 60 cm for elite male soccer players (Green 1992, Wisløff et al. 1998). Raven et al. (1976) used one repetition maximum bench press to test muscle strength of male players and reported a mean value of 73 kg. High levels of maximal strength in upper and lower limbs may prevent injuries in soccer by increasing strength and mobility of tendon and ligaments (Reilly 1994a,b). Most of the research in the area of endurance and strength has been conducted using male subjects. There is an obvious lack of results for female athletes reported as 1-RM, vertical jump height and sprint times. The conclusions and recommendations, therefore, have an inherent gender bias.

The major purpose of the present study was to examine gender differences in cardiovascular endurance capacity as well as muscular strength and power in the best male- and female soccer teams in Norway. Maximal oxygen uptake and strength in proportion to body mass for soccer players were further investigated. A secondary aim was to establish normative data of elite female soccer players.

Methods

One male and one female team from Norwegian premier league participated in the study. The male team, Rosenborg, is the most successful team in the soccer premier league in Norway the last 8 years and is also presently successful in the European Champions League. The female team Trondheims-Ørn is the most successful female team in Norway, delivering almost half of the national team squad, at the moment being reigning world champions. Physiological assessments were made of 14 male players and 12 female players in their preparatory training phase. Eight of the male players and eigth of the female players have played for the national team or the Olympic team (under 23 yr.). Each subject reviewed and signed consent forms approved by the Human Research Review Committee before participating in the study. Physical and physiological characteristics of the subjects are presented in Table 1. All of the players within a given team were assessed on the same day, and the tests were performed in the same order. Vertical jumping height was determined using a force platform and BioWare calculations as centre of mass displacement (Kistler, Switzerland) with hands placed on the waist. Squat 1RM was tested to 90 degrees knee angle, using free weights (Eleiko, Sweden). Heart rate (f_c) was determined using short-range radio telemetry (Polar Sporttester, Polar Electro, Finland). Oxygen uptake (VO_2), minute ventilation and breathing frequency were measured during work using an Ergo Oxyscreen (Jaeger EOS sprint, Germany) using previously described protocols (Helgerud et al. 1990). Allometric equations was used to determine the relationship between maximal oxygen uptake/maximal strength and body mass; $VO_2 = a \cdot m_b^b$ and $1RM = a \cdot m_b^b$, where a is the mass coefficient, m_b is the bodymass in kilos and b is the reduced exponent, the numerical value of which can be obtained from the log-log plot of the experimental data, since the logarithmic expression is a straight line ($\log VO_2$ or $\log 1RM = \log a + b \cdot \log m_b^b$) (Åstrand and Rodahl 1986).

Table 1. Physical and physiological characteristics of players

	Age	Height (cm)	Mass (kg)	[Hb] ($g \cdot dl^{-1}$)	Hct (%)	VC (liters)	FEV_1/VC (%)	f_{cmax} (beats · min^{-1}
Rosenborg (n=14)	23.9 (4.3	181.1 (4.9)	76.9 (6.3)	15.0 (0.8)	45.8 (2.1)	5.32 (0.68)	90.5 (5.0)	192 (7.6)
Trondh-Ørn (n=12)	22.3 (2.7	169.7 (7.1)	62.5 (7.4)	13.7 (0.9)	44.2 (2.6)	4.15 (0.52)	87.8 (6.0)	190 (4.7)

[Hb]; hemoglobin concentration in blood, Hct; hematocrit, VC; vital capacity, FEV_1; forced expiratory volume in 1 second, f_{cmax}; maximal heart rate.

Results

Rosenborg players had of course absolute values concerned as capacities for soccer performance higher than the female players from Trondheims-Ørn (Table 2). There was a significant correlation between 1RM expressed per $kg^{0.75}$ and vertical jumping height for the male soccer players ($r= 0.67$, $p<0.05$), but not for the female soccer players.

Table 2. Comparison of results between the two teams

Team	VO_{2max}			Squats		
	$l \cdot min^{-1}$	$ml \cdot kg^{-1} \cdot min^{-1}$	$ml \cdot kg^{-0.75} \cdot min^{-1}$	(kg)	$(kg \cdot m_b^{-1})$	$(kg \cdot m_b^{-0.67})$
Rosenborg (n=14)	5.20 (0.40)	67.6 (4.0)	200.2 (8.4)	164.6 (21.8)	2.1 (0.3)	9.0 (1.2)
Trondh-Ørn (n=12)	3.36 (0.37)	54.0 (3.54)	151.5 (9.3)	112.5 (20.7)	1.8 (0.3)	7.1 (1.3)

Team	Benchpress			Vertical jump
	(kg)	$(kg \cdot m_b^{-1})$	$(kg \cdot m_b^{-0.67})$	(cm)
Rosenborg (n=14)	82.7(12.8)	1.1 (0.3)	4.6 (0.7)	56.7 (6.6)
Trondh-Ørn (n=12)	43.8(5.1)	0.7 (0.1)	2.7 (0.3)	42.9 (3.3)

All of Rosenborg results are significantly higher than Trondheims-Ørn ($p<0.05$), VO_{2max}; maximal oxygen uptake.

Neither VO_{2max} nor maximal strength does increase proportionally to body mass in elite soccer players. The exponent b was found to be significantly less than unity for both male and female players. VO_{2max} increased proportional to $kg^{0.79}$ for females and $kg^{0.66}$ for males. 1RM squat increased proportional to $kg^{0.55}$ for men whereas there were no correlation for females.

1RM bench press increased proportional to $kg^{0.74}$ for Rosenborgs' male players, but no correlation was found for Trondheims-Ørns' female players.

Discussion

Mean $\dot{V}O_{2max}$ for Rosenborg and Trondheims-Ørn is in the upper range of values normally reported for male and female soccer players respectively (Davies and Brewer 1993, Wisløff et al 1998). This may reflect that the volume and methods of training in soccer have been improved. The gender differences in $\dot{V}O_{2max}$ in the present study are about the same as found in the average population (10-15 $ml \cdot kg^{-1} \cdot min^{-1}$)(Åstrand and Rodahl 1986). This reflects that the two teams are equally well trained. Compared to other sports, VO2max values in the present study is not very high. It is thus the author's view that soccer trainers should try to elevate the aerobic power of their team.

The $\dot{V}O_{2max}$ was inversely related to body mass (m_b) in both men and women. The reduced exponents were close to the value of $m_b^{0.67}$ based on dimensional analysis. Thus, the conventional method of expressing $\dot{V}O_{2max}$ per kg will penalize heavy individuals (Åstrand and Rodahl 1986). To avoid introducing yet another exponent it seems reasonable to concur with the conclusions of Bergh et al. (1991) and express $\dot{V}O_{2max}$ in relation to $m_b^{0.75}$ when running (Wisløff et al 1998). The dimensional scaling approach will improve female values for $\dot{V}O_{2max}$ from being 65% ($l \cdot min^{-1}$) to being 75% ($ml \cdot kg^{-0.75} \cdot min^{-1}$) of male values. Lower blood hemoglobin concentration among female soccer player's accounts for some of the gender difference. Considerable differences exist for respiratory volumes between sexes and no differences are to be noted in maximal heart rate, which is in line with previous studies (Helgerud 1994).

In the present study the female maximal strength in squats was 68% of the result for the male team, in absolute terms. Corrected for size, the capacity to move oneself in jumps and sprints, i.e. the relative strength, for the female players was 79% of the male players, which shows that a big part of strength differences is really size difference. In terms of performance though, absolute size and strength is determining the outcome. Female vertical jumping height was 76% of the male results, which is in the lower part of differences reported. For benchpress the female weights lifted was 53% of the male performance, but also here a part of the performance difference is a size difference. Corrected for size, the female relative benchpress values are 59% of the male values. Both results are in the range of what is normally reported as gender differences.

Differences between male and female elite soccer teams in physical resources determined as endurance and strength parameters seem to be in the same range as reported as sedentary gender differences. This means that compared to sedentary counterparts within the same gender, the female elite soccer players seem to have improved as much as the male elite soccer player. There is thus no reason to claim that female soccer is shortcoming compared to elite male soccer in terms of strength and endurance.

References

Balsom, P. (1994) Evaluation of physical performance. In: B. Ekblom (ed) Football (Soccer). Blackwell Scientific Publications, 102-123.

Bangsbo, J., Nørregaard, L. and Thorsøe, F. (1991) Active profile of competition soccer. *Can.J.Sports Sci.,* 16: 110-116.

Bergh, U., Sjødin, B., Forsberg, A., and Svedenhag, J. (1991) The relationship between body mass and oxygen uptake during running in humans. *Med. Sci. Sports. Exerc.*,

23:205-211

Bührle, M. and Schmidtbleicer, D. (1977) Der einfluss von maximalkrafttraining auf die bewegungsschnelligkeit (The influence of maximum strength training on movement velocity). *Leistungssport*, 7: 3-10.

Cureton, K.J., Bishop, P., Hutchinson, P., Newland, H., Vickery, S., Zwiren, L. (1986) Sex difference in maximal oxygen uptake: Effect of equating hemoglobin concentration. *Eur. J. Appl. Physiol.,* 54: 656-660.

Davis, J.A. and Brewer, J. (1993) Applied physiology of female soccer players. *Sport Med.*, 16: 180-189.

Davies, J.A., Brewer,J., and Atkin, D. (1992) Pre-season physiological characteristics of English first and second division soccer players. *J. Sport Sci.,* 10: 541-547.

Green, S. (1992) Anthropometric and physiological characteristics of South Australian soccer players. *Aus.J. Sci. Med. Sport.*, 24: 3-7.

Helgerud, J. (1994) Maximal oxygen uptake, anaerobic threshold and running economy in women with similar performances level in marathons. *Eur. J. Appl. Physiol.,* 68: 155-161.

Helgerud, J., Ingjer, F., and Strømme, S.B. (1990) Sex differences in performance-matched marathon runners. *Eur. J. Appl. Physiol.,* 61: 433-439.

Hoff, J. and Almåsbakk, B.(1995) The effects of maximum strength training on throwing velocity and muscle strength in female team-handball players. *J. Strength. Cond. Res.*, 9: 255-258.

Raven, P., Gettman, L., Pollock, M., and Cooper, K. (1976) A physiological evaluation of professional soccer players. *Br. J. Sports Med.*, 109: 209-216.

Reilly, T. (1994a) Motion characteristics. In: B. Ekblom (ed) Football (Soccer). Blackwell Scientific Publications, 31-43.

Reilly, T. (1994b) Physiological profile of the player: In: B. Ekblom (ed) Football (Soccer). Blackwell Scientific Publications, 78-95.

Schmidtbleicher, D. (1992) Training for power events. In: P. Komi (ed.) Strength and power in sport, 381-395.

Döbeln, W. von (1956) Maximal oxygen uptake, body size and total hemoglobin in normal
man. *Acta Physiol. Scand.* 95: 153-165

Wisløff, U., Helgerud, J. and Hoff, J. (1998) Strength and endurance of elite soccer players. *Med. Sci. Sports Exerc.*, 30(3): 462-467.

Åstrand, P.-O., and Rodahl, K. (1986) "Textbook of work physiology". McGraw-Hill Book Company, New York.

Accepted for publication in: Scand J Med Sci Sports

NON-DOMINANT LEG TRAINING IMPROVES THE BILATERAL MOTOR PERFORMANCE OF SOCCER PLAYERS

HAALAND, Eilif[1] and HOFF, Jan[2]

[1] Stadion Medical Practice, Bergen, Norway

[2] Norwegian University of Science and Technology, Department of Physiology and Biomedical Engineering, Trondheim, Norway

Running head: Bilateral motor performance.

Abstract

The aim of this experiment was to evaluate bilateral motor performance effects from training the non-dominant leg of competitive soccer players. The subjects were 39 soccer players, 15 to 20 years of age, performance-matched and randomly divided into an experimental group (n=18) and a control group (n=21) both belonging to the same team. Both groups were tested by using two standardised foot-tapping tests and three soccer-specific tests. The training intervention consisted of the experimental group participating in all parts of their soccer training except full play, using the non-dominant leg for 8 weeks.

Statistical analyses for the soccer-specific tests revealed that the experimental group improved significantly as compared to the control group from the pre-test to the post-test period in their use of the trained non-dominant leg. Somewhat unexpectedly, the experimental group also improved significantly in the tests which made use of the dominant side. The standardized foot-tapping tests revealed similar results. The results might be explained by improved generalized motor programmes, or from a Dynamic Systems Approach, indicating that the actual training relates to the handling of all the information available to the subject in the situation, and that the body self-organizes the motor performance.

Key words: Dominant, non-dominant, learning, training, motor skill.

Introduction

The ability to learn a particular skill more easily with one hand or leg after the skill has been learned with the opposite hand or leg is related to what is known as bilateral transfer (Magill, 1995). The bulk of evidence supporting bilateral transfer was published during the 1930s, mainly by Cook (1933; 1936), who referred to the phenomenon as 'cross education'. Bilateral transfer is traditionally accounted for as the transference of common elements of the task (Ammons, 1958), based on Thorndike's 'identical elements'. Two explanations are used for bilateral transfer, a cognitive explanation and a motor control explanation. The cognitive explanation is related to the knowledge of 'what to do' to achieve the goal of a skill. Support for the cognitive element is given in Kohl and Roenker (1980), where bilateral transfer was shown both for a unilateral training group and a mental training group, but not for a control group not familiar with the task. There are two ways of considering the motor control explanation. The first is the traditional motor programme perspective, where the memory representation is responsible for the class of movements or actions and would in principle be available for both limbs. The second is grounded in a Dynamic Systems perspective, where time and space features of the movement act as control mechanisms in an integrated perception-action coupling (Kelso, 1995). Raibert (1977) has shown movement pattern similarities for writing signatures by hand regardless of which body parts execute the skill, a finding which can provide support for both views.

Provins and Glencross (1968) have shown that professional typewriters in a typewriting task have slightly better performances when they use their left hand, whereas non-typists have significantly better performances when they use their right hand. When the same groups were given a simple handwriting task, both groups recorded a highly significant difference in performance between the two sides in favour of the preferred hand. These findings are strong indications that differences between hands might be a function of practice rather than genetic predispositions. However, whether the development of a dominant side of the body is a function of nature or nurture is still under debate (Provins, 1997).

There is no doubt that a high degree of skill in using both feet improves the ability to carry out soccer motor performance. This is a paradigm example which indicates that bilateral skill development in several sport situations is an important aspect of training. Players seldom use both limbs with equal emphasis, and develop a preferred side which represents the subject's 'handedness', or, rather, 'footedness', in terms of soccer performance, as is also developed in most everyday motor skills.

Peters (1976, 1981) has reported improvements in the performance of the dominant hand after training the non-dominant hand. Peters (1976) suggests, in an attempt to explain these findings, that the level of skill in the dominant hand might be restricted by the level of the same skill on the non-dominant side. This is a point of departure for this experiment. The first hypothesis is that increased use of the non-dominant leg in training will improve both general and soccer-specific skills when using the non-dominant leg. The second hypothesis is that training the non-dominant leg will enhance both general and soccer-specific skills in the use of the dominant leg.

Methods

Subjects

47 male competitive soccer players participated in the study from the outset. Exclusion criteria were a minimum of 75% of the training intervention carried out in the training group, and participation in both pre and post-test periods. 39 male players, ranging from 15 to 21 years of age, matched by age groups, and randomly assigned to an experimental group (n=18) and a control group (n=21) completed the study. Most of the subjects were from a boy's team (15 and 16 years of age) n=8 and n=9. Juniors (17 and 18 years of age) were n= 6 and n=8, and seniors (19+ years of age) were n=4 and n=4 in the experimental group and the control group respectively. They were all right-handed and right-footed, based on self-reports. All players reviewed and signed consent forms approved by the Human Research Review Committee prior to participating in the study. Due to injuries, two of the subjects in the training group and one subject in the control group did not perform all of the tests. Degrees of freedom thus vary from 35 to 37 in the different tests.

Tests

Three soccer performance tests were carried out, using either leg. The soccer test was carried out on an excellent grass soccer field in good weather conditions. Two standardized foot-tapping tests were performed, using the preferred and the non-preferred leg consecutively, indoors in a separate testing room with only the test administrator present. The persons collecting the data were blinded to the group allocations. The soccer tests were carried out in randomized order. All soccer tests were carried out before the standardized foot-tapping tests. The foot-tapping tests were also randomized. The coefficients of variation for the five tests used were calculated through the use of another group of male soccer players as subjects, n=15, 18 (SD 1,1) years of age. They were tested on two consecutive days, following the same test routine as described for the experiment (Sale, 1991).

Test a. A slalom dribble test back and forth from a starting point with a 1-metre distance to and from the first marker, between 5 markers on a line with a distance of 1 metre between them, and around the last marker. The inside and outside of one foot were used. The subjects carried out two trials with each leg. There was a 4-minute interval between trials. The time used to complete a trial was measured by using a hand-held stopwatch. The time for both trials on each leg was aggregated. If the player lost the ball, the test continued until two successful trials were accomplished. The coefficient of variation for the dribbling test was 4.3%.

Test b. A receiving and direct volley shot test. The subject received the ball at breast height in front of the goal, with his side facing the goal, at a distance of 10 metres. The ball was received and a volley shot was the second touch at the ball. Points were given for where the shot was placed in the goal. The goal itself and a zone 30 cm outside the goal were divided into zones giving from 6 points in the top corners to 1 point for a shot where the goalkeeper normally stands, and 1 point also for a hit on the ground within 30 cm of the goal (Figure 1). Points were added for 15 + 15 shots with each leg. There was a 4-minute rest between trials. The coefficient of variation for the volley shot test was 11.5%.

Distance metre	*0.3*	*1.2*	*1.2*	*2.2*	*1.2*	*1.2*	*0.3*
0.3	4	3	2	1	2	3	4
0.8	3	6	4	3	4	6	3
0.8	2	5	2	1	2	5	2
0.8	1	4	2	1	2	4	1

Figure 1. Point matrix for a 10 m shot against a soccer goal.

Test c. A one-touch passing test. The distance was 10 metres from a mini-goal which was 1 m wide and 40 cm high. A pass was received from the right and left-hand sides respectively. The definition of a successful pass was that the ball had to be rolling, not jumping, and that the ball moved until the pass was completed. Unsuccessful passes to the subject were not counted. The ball was passed on one touch towards the goal. 15 + 15 trials with each leg, with a 3-minute break. 1 point per hit in the goal. Both trials were counted. The coefficient of variation for the one-touch passing test was 11.3%.

Test d. A standardized foot-tapping test. The subjects were seated in a chair. The foot was moved sideways on the floor between two 15 x 15 cm quadrates with a centre distance of 30 cm. 15 repetitions were timed by using a hand-held stopwatch. Two series, using each leg, were performed. The time used for two series was aggregated. If there were mishaps in a series, the testing continued until two successful series were completed. The coefficient of variation for the standardized two-way foot-tapping test was 4.5%.

Test e. A standardized foot-tapping test. Like test d, but with three positions. The first quadrate was located vertically under the knee, the next 30 cm ahead and the third 30 cm sideways from the quadrate ahead. Tapping was carried out back and forth. Two series of 25 touches each with each foot were executed. The series were timed by using a hand-held stopwatch. The aggregate time for both trials was used. If there were mishaps in a series, the testing continued until two successful series were completed. The coefficient of variation for the standardized 3-way foot-tapping test was 4.5%.

Procedure

A pre-test – post-test control group design was used. Intervention consisted of increased volume of soccer training with the left, non-preferred leg for a period of 8 weeks. The training did not consist of specific practice on the tests used in the experiment, but general use of the left leg in all individual technical training. Dependent variables were the performance scores, using the described tests. A standardized 10-minute warm-up period using different forms of running was carried out prior to the tests. The subjects were kept ignorant of the hypothesis and the purpose of the training intervention. The test personnel were not present during training, to avoid "Hawthorne"-effects.

Statistical analysis

A statistical analysis was carried out, using SPSS 6.0 for Windows. The data were analysed with repeated measures analysis of variance. The statistical significance was accepted at

$P<0.05$. The descriptive statistics include means and standard deviations (SD). T-tests for paired samples were used to evaluate differences between groups before training intervention.

Results

The results from pre and post-test periods for the soccer-specific dribbling test for both legs are presented as mean and standard deviations (SD) in Figure 2. A significant group x time interaction was found for the dribbling performance using the left leg, the subject for the training intervention [$F(1,35)= 15.82$; $P=0.000$]. The improvement from pre to post-test periods was 10.3%, 7.3% over the control group. For the dominant leg (right), which was not emphasized more than in normal soccer, a significant group x time interaction was found for the dribbling test when using the dominant (right) leg [$F(1,36)= 9.05$; $P=0.004$]. The improvement was 7.8%, 6.5% over the control group. There were no initial differences between the groups.

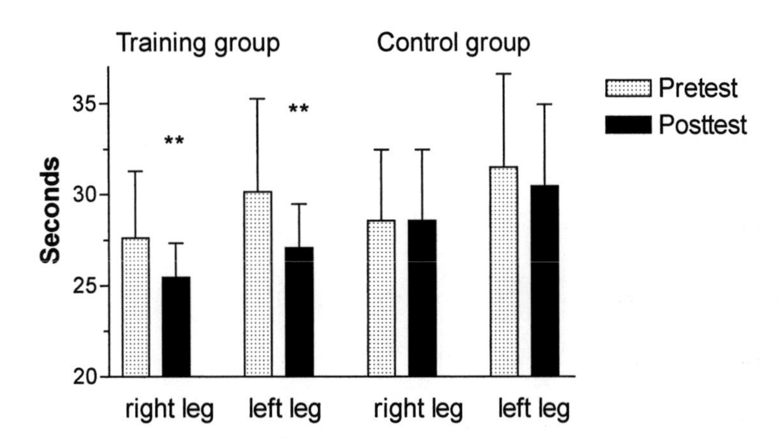

Figure 2. Pre and post-test for the training group with left leg soccer training intervention and the control group, using the right and the left leg in the soccer-specific test a: dribble test. * = $p<0.05$, **= $p<0.01$.

For test b, the volley shot at a goal, significant group x time interaction was found in the use of the left leg [$F(1,35)= 7.25; P=0.010$], a 25.4% improvement, 18.5% over the control group. A significant group x time interaction was also found in the use of the dominant (right) leg [$F(1,35)= 8.27; P=0.006$] (Figure 3), an improvement of 28.6% , 34.9% over the control group. There were no initial differences between the groups.

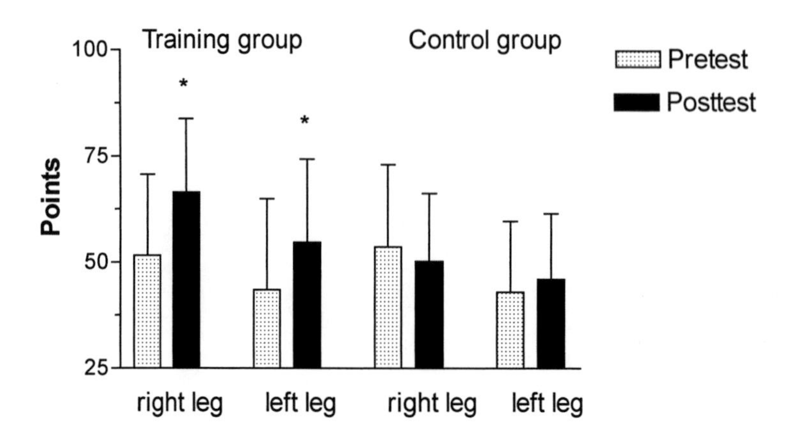

Figure 3. Pre and post-test for the training group with left leg soccer training intervention and the control group, using the right and the left leg in the soccer-specific test b: volley goal shot. * = p<0.05, **= p<0.01.

For test c, the mini goal point shot, a significant group x time interaction for the left leg was found [$F(1,37)= 6.14; P=0.017$], an improvement 11.3%, 12.0% over the control group. When using the right leg, a significant group x time interaction was found [$F(1,36)= 7.93; P=0.007$] (Figure 4), an improvement of 13.1%, 2% over the control group. There were no initial differences between the groups.

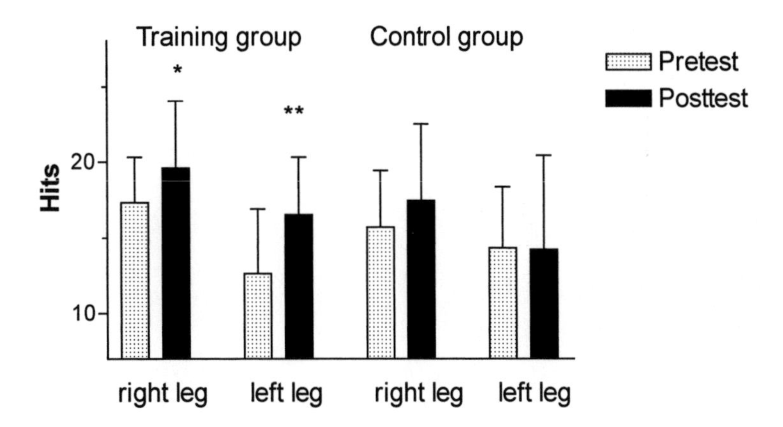

Figure 4. Pre and post-test for the training group with left leg soccer training intervention and the control group, using the right and the left leg in the soccer-specific test c: passing against a mini goal. * = p<0.05, **= p<0.01.

Results from pre and post-test periods for the non-soccer-specific tests are presented as mean and standard deviation (SD) in Figures 5 and 6. For the two-point foot-tapping test using sideways foot and leg movements, a significant group x time interaction was found for the left, non-dominant leg [$F(1,36)= 42.10$; $P=0.000$], an improvement of 11.9%, 3.7% over the control group. For the right leg [$F(1,36)= 28.15$; $P=0.000$] (Figure 5), an improvement of 12.5%, 6.4% over the control group was found. There were no initial differences between the groups.

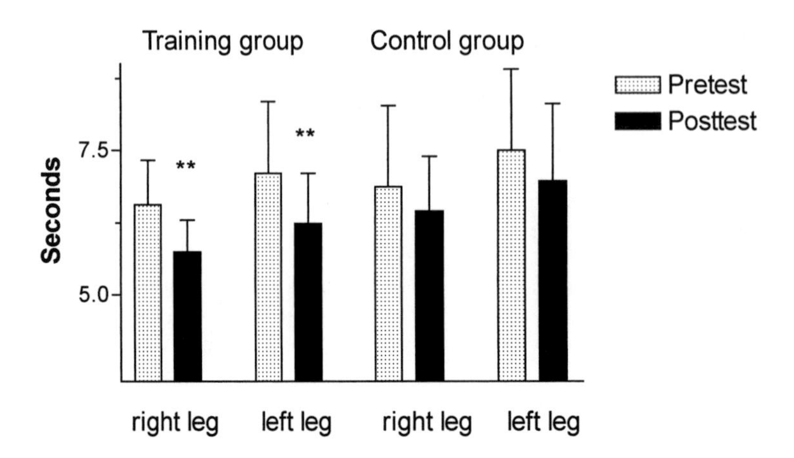

Figure 5. Pre- and post-test for the training group with left leg soccer training intervention and the control group, using the right and the left leg in the standardized foot-tapping test d: two position foot-tapping. * = p<0.05, **= p<0.01.

For test e, the more complicated standardized foot-tapping test with three points to hit, a significant time x group interaction was found in the use of the left leg [$F(1,36)= 42.10$; P=0.000], an improvement of 7.6%, 5.7% over the control group. Significant group x time interaction was found in the use of the dominant (right) leg [$F(1,36)= 13.32$; P=0.000] (Figure 6), an improvement of 8.2%, 5% over the control group. There were no initial differences between the groups.

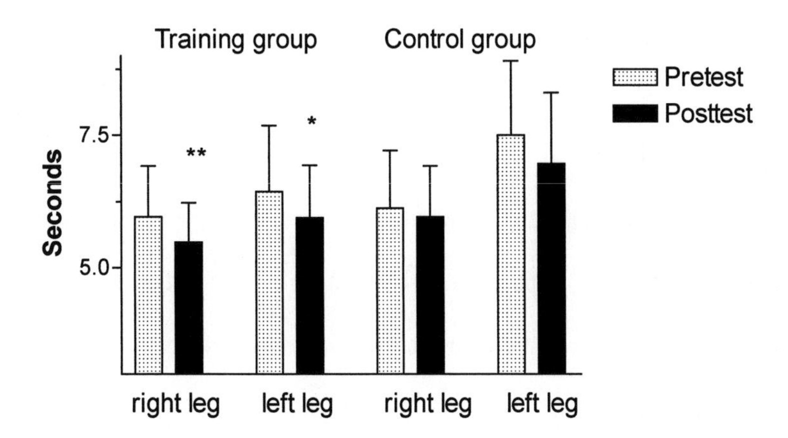

Figure 6. Pre and post-test for the training group with left leg soccer training intervention and the control group, using the right and the left leg in the standardized foot-tapping test d: three position foot-tapping. * = $p<0.05$, **= $p<0.01$.

The control group did not improve significantly in any of the soccer-specific tests which were used as dependent variables. A significant improvement was found, however, in the simplest of the standardized foot-tapping tests, test d, using the non-dominant foot.

Total training time in the 8-week intervention period was for the training group 2768 minutes (SD = 506 minutes), of which the training group used the left leg for 705 minutes (SD = 85 minutes). The control group trained during the intervention period for 2803 minutes (SD = 503 minutes) and reported using the left leg for 73 minutes (SD = 32 minutes). Almost all the training performed in the 8-week period was training with the team. The training group reported 183 minutes (SD 153 minutes) of individual training, and the control group reported 125 minutes (SD 77 minutes) of individual training.

Discussion

Enhanced training which uses the non-dominant leg improves soccer-specific skills in the test where the subjects use this leg , a finding which stands in contrast to the results of a control group. This is in line with the first hypothesis. Also the general foot-tapping test results using the non-dominant foot are improved after a period of soccer training with emphasis on the use of the non-dominant leg. The improvement is not a test-retest effect, as the improvement lies well above the results of a control group which also participates in both test and retest.

That the training group also showed statistically significant improvements over the control group when using the dominant (right) leg was in line with the second hypothesis. The results show an improvement in performance when using the dominant leg after a period of emphasizing training of the non-dominant leg. This finding is not entirely in line with general scientific findings, which often show a high degree of specificity in motor learning (Magill, 1993). However, the results are in line with Peters (1976; 1981). Peters (1976) trained one subject, practising a daily routine at the rate of 20 trials per day with the index finger of each hand, for a total of 1300 trials. Whereas the right hand's tapping rate was some 6.5% faster than that of the left at the beginning of the experiment, after about 1200 trials, the left was as fast as the right. The marked improvement in performance was recorded for both hands. In a follow-up study (Peters, 1981), improvements in the performance of the dominant hand after training the non-dominant hand were also reported. The results in this experiment might be seen to support the suggestion that the level of skill on the non-dominant side might restrict the level of skill in the use of the dominant side.

Overall, the tests for the training group show that the skills in using the non-dominant (left) leg develops to about the level of skill that was shown in using the dominant leg in the pre-test period. It might be worth noticing that the differences between the right and the left leg are of a similar magnitude after the training period. It might be surprising that the control group during 8 weeks of soccer training did not show improvements in any of the soccer-specific tests. One might question the quality of the soccer training, or argue that the selection of soccer-relevant tests does not represent soccer as it is normally played, or question the fruitfulness of the elements that were emphasized during that particular period of soccer training.

A simple interpretation of the results might lend support to a motor programme perspective (Schmidt, 1976), where one envisages that the training improves a general motor programme that is available to both the right and the left side. The control group, however, spent an equal amount of time and used the same exercises as the training group. An eventual generalized motor programme should have more opportunities to be improved by the use of the dominant leg, since the skills in using this leg has a higher level from the beginning.

One possible approach to the findings in this experiment is that training the non-dominant leg leads to increased attention being paid to the training situation on the part of the subjects. A training effect from a higher degree of attention might not be difficult to understand from a theoretical point of view within a Dynamic Systems Approach (DSA) (Kelso, 1995). DSA, which is based on the self-organization of brain and behaviour, is, to judge by the volume of research, the dominating model for explaining development of motor learning and control at present. If one take into account all the perceptual information that is available in addition to the motor variables, cross education need not be surprising, and needs no “ghost in the machinery” or homunculus explanation. What seems to be learned in motor skills is dependent upon perception-action coupling, which in a DSA-perspective is to pick up relevant information within the optical flow field (Gibson, 1979). This relevant information does not only contain such physical variables as velocity, displacement or mass, but rather higher order information. Variables of a higher order can be invariants in the optical flow field, i.e. they appear with shifts both in time and context. Invariant variables of a stable character in the environment are elements such as texture gradients (Gibson, 1979), the direct rate of change of size of an object on retina (tau – information) (Lee, 1976; Lee, Young, Reddish, Lough and Clayton, 1983; Lee, Reddish and Rand, 1991; Lee, Davis, Green, and van der Weel,1993; Bootsma, Mestre and Bakker, 1994) and relative mass (Jacobs, Michels and Runeson, 1998). What seems to be important for the learner is to perceive relevant information in the situation, which in turn contains both environment and subject. This sum of information forms the situation from which the subject chooses actions to improve a motor performance. What the soccer player does should be viewed in a context of him relating to invariants in perceptual information and learning to pick up relevant information for the specific situation. Even if the actions themselves are crucial for improving the performance, a dynamic systems approach would be to take what information is perceived, what is relevant information, as a basis for the muscular self-organization. This muscular self-organization is available for both the dominant and the non-dominant side. Improved performance is in this context a function of the players’ ability to learn to relate to relevant information of which the task is dependent, and that the action or behaviour itself is primarily self-organized. From this, it is easier to understand that increased attention when training the non-dominant leg might imply that the subjects are trained to pick up relevant information in the environment during the training session, and that this information is available for a high degree of self-organization, and for use with both the dominant and the non-dominant side. In a DSA-perspective, the conclusion and explanation of cross education is that the soccer player learns to pick up relevant information in the coupling between the environment and himself, rather than an improvement in a generalized cognitive structure, such as a motor programme.

A development of skills in using the non-dominant side might also give more possibilities and a higher degree of security when choosing between actions on the soccer field. This might also explain parts of the findings in this experiment.

The dominant hand and the dominant leg normally, but not always, correspond among soccer players. Limited amounts of training, as typically seen in training experiments, might not be sufficient for developing changes, compared to the long-term effects of preferences in everyday situations. As a consequence, one consistent finding is that performances with the preferred hand are superior to the non-preferred side (Annett, 1985). As Crossman (1959), Ericsson, Krampe and Tesch-Romer (1993) and Klemmer (1962) have shown, improvements in occupational or professional motor skills continue for millions of trials. It is thus necessary to consider the individual performances of each hand on unimanual and bimanual tasks that have been subject to a lifetime of experience or similar extensive practice to obtain a more accurate and relevant estimate of the effects of training. Whether the development of a dominant side of the body is a function of nature or nurture will probably still be under debate for a long period of time.

Whatever theoretical model is used for trying to understand cross education and the findings in this experiment, there is reason to be aware of the strong performance effects of using the non-dominant leg in training. The findings also imply that training the other side of the body during a period of injury or disease might have a substantial effect. The practical applications from the findings in this experiment are obvious: soccer players and coaches should put more emphasis on training the "wrong" leg in order to improve their soccer skills with both the right and the left leg.

Acknowledgements

The technical assistance from Professor Bernt E. Engelsen, Department of Neurology, Haukeland University Hospital, Bergen and statistical assistance from Professor Stein H. Lygre, University of Bergen, Norway are highly appreciated.

References

Ammons R.B. (1958) Le mouvement. In G.H. Steward and J.P. Steward (Eds) Current psychological issues (pp 146-183) Henry Holt & Co. New York

Annett M. (1985) Left, right, hand and brain. The right shift theory. Erlbaum. London

Bootsma, R. J., Mestre, D.R. & Bakker, F.C. (1994) Catching Balls: How to Get the Hand to the Right Place at the Right Time. *J Experimental Psych: Human Perception and Performance*, 3, 591-612

Cook T.W. (1933) Studies in cross education II. Further experimentation in mirror tracing the star shaped maze. *J Experimental Psych* 16: 670-700

Cook T.W. (1936) Studies in cross education V. Theoretical. *Psych Review* 43:149-178

Crossman E.R.F.W. (1959) A theory of the acquisition of speed-skill. *Ergonomics* 2: 153-166

Ericsson K.A., Krampe R.T. and Tesch-Romer C. (1993) The role of deliberate practice in the acquisition of expert performance. *Psychological Review* 100: 363-406

Gibson, J.J. (1979) The ecological approach to visual perception. Boston: Houghton Mifflin.

Jacobs, D.M., Michaels, C.F. & Runeson, S. (1998). Perceptual learning and its importance for the visual perception of relative mass. In: B. Bril (Ed.) Advances in Perception-Action Coupling. Paris: EDK.

Kelso J.A.S. (1995) Dynamic patterns. The self-organisation of brain and behavior. MIT Press. Cambridge

Klemmer E.T. (1962) Communication and human performance. *Human Factors* 4:75-79

Kohl R.M. and Roenker D.M. (1980) Bilateral transfer as a function of mental imagery. *J Motor Behavior* 12:197-206

Lee, D.N. (1976). A theory of visual control of braking based on information about time-to-collision, *Perception*, 5, 437-459

Lee, D.N., Davis, M.O., Green, P.R. & van der Weel, R. (1993) Visual control of approach by pigeons when landing, *J Experimental Biology*, 180: 85-104.

Lee, D.N., Young, D.S., Reddish, P.E., Lough, S. & Clayton, T.M.H. (1983) Visual timing in hitting an accelerating ball. *Quart J Experimental Psych* 35A: 333-346

Lee, D.N., Reddish, P.E. & Rand, D.T. (1991) Aerial Docking by Hummingbirds, *Naturwissenshaften*, 78, 526-527

Magill R.A. (1993) Motor learning. Concepts and Applications. Brown and Benchmark, Indiana

Peters M. (1976) Prolonged practice of a simple motor task by preferred and non-preferred hands. *Perc Motor Skills* 43: 447-450

Peters M. (1981) Handedness: Effect of prolonged practice between hand performance differences. *Neuropsych* 19: 587-590

Provins K.A. (1997) The specificity of motor skill and manual asymmetry: A review of the evidence and its implications. *J Motor Behavior* 29(2): 183-192

Provins K.A. and Glencross D.J. (1968) Handwriting, typewriting and handedness. *Quart J Experimental Psych* 20:282-289

Raibert M. (1977) Motor control and learning by the state-space model. Technical report. Artificial Intelligence Laboratory, Massachusetts Institute of Technology (AI-TR-439)

Sale D.G. (1991) Testing Strength and Power. In: MacDougall D., Wenger H.A., Green H.J. (eds) Physiological Testing of the High-Performance Athlete (pp 74-75) Human Kinetics, Champaign, Ill.

Schmidt R.A. (1976) The schema as a solution to some persistent problems in motor learning theory. In G.E.Stelmach (Ed.), Motor Control: Issues and trends (pp 41-65) Academic Press. New York